David McHugh

ESSENTIALS

GCSE D&T

Electronic Products

Contents

Contents

Integrated Circuits

PIC Microcontrollers and Infra-red Control

Plastics

Plastics

1 Name the two groups that plastics are divided into.

a) ....

b) ....

Main Properties of Plastics

2 Name three main properties of plastics.

a) ....

b) ....

c) ....

Thermoplastics and Thermosetting Plastics

3 Choose the correct words from the options given to complete the sentences below.

GRP   Nylon   Acrylic   Epoxy resin   HIPS   PVC   ABS

a) The trade name for .... is Perspex. It's used for aircraft windows, washbasins and baths, and it easily cracks and scratches.

b) .... is self-lubricating and is used for bearings and gear wheels.

c) .... is used for canoes, boats and car bodies.

d) .... is used for pipes, guttering and window frames.

e) .... is used for car parts, tool handles and kitchenware and is highly resistant to impact.

f) .... is used for toys, boxes and containers and can be injection moulded, vacuum formed and blow moulded.

g) .... is used for making PCBs.

Timbers

1 Name the three groups that timbers are divided into and name a timber for each group.

Group	Example of Timber
a)	
b)	
c)	

Main Properties of Timber

2 Explain the following properties of timber.

a) Workability

b) Texture

c) Grain Pattern

Types of Timber

3 Draw lines between the boxes to match each timber to its description.

MDF	The most widely used timber for general purpose work. Can be nailed without splitting the wood and joined with screws and PVA glue.
Plywood	Widely used in furniture for bedrooms and kitchens. Useful for creating moulds for vacuum forming. Made by bonding wood fibres with resin-based adhesive.
Hardwoods	Constructed from an odd number of thin layers glued together. Has a uniform strength throughout. Stronger when it has a greater number of layers.
Pine	Include mahogany and beech.

Metals

Metals and Their Properties

1 Circle the correct options in the following sentences.

   a) Non-ferrous metals **contain / don't contain** iron and **are / aren't** attracted to magnets.

   b) Ferrous metals **contain / don't contain** iron and **are / aren't** attracted to magnets.

2 **a)** What is tensile strength?

     ....

   b) What is ductility?

     ....

Non-ferrous and Ferrous Metals

3 Match statements **A**, **B** and **C** with the terms **1–3** in the table. Enter the appropriate number in the boxes provided.

   A Are attracted to a magnet. Consist mainly of iron. ◯

   B Contain two or more metals. Brass is a typical example. ◯

   C Contain no iron at all. Copper and aluminium are examples. ◯

	Term
1	Alloys
2	Ferrous Metals
3	Non-ferrous Metals

4 Draw lines between the boxes to match each metal to its properties.

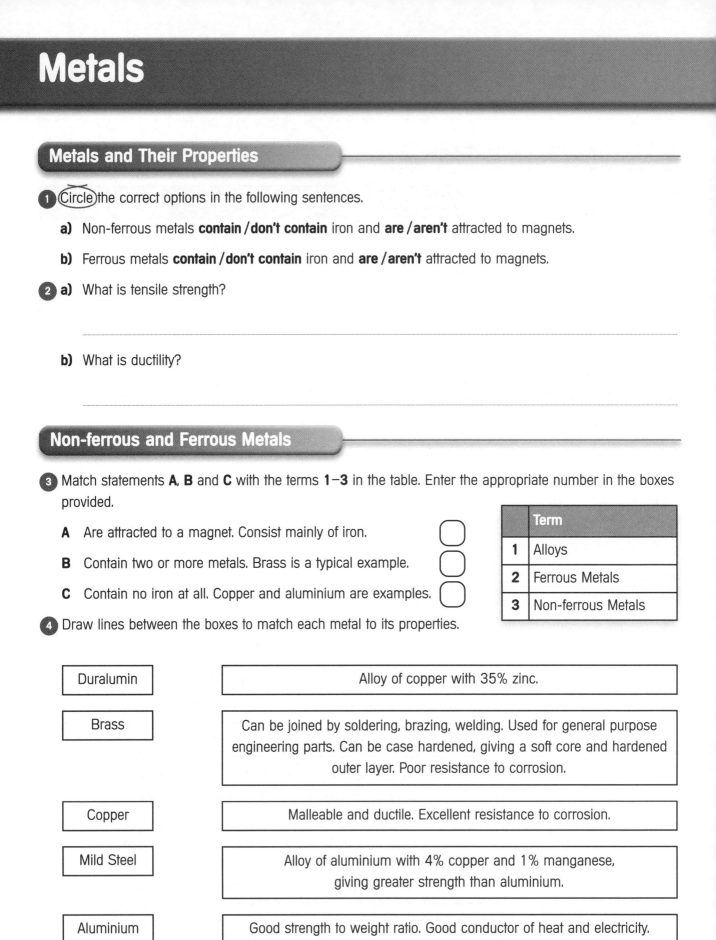

| Duralumin | Alloy of copper with 35% zinc. |

| Brass | Can be joined by soldering, brazing, welding. Used for general purpose engineering parts. Can be case hardened, giving a soft core and hardened outer layer. Poor resistance to corrosion. |

| Copper | Malleable and ductile. Excellent resistance to corrosion. |

| Mild Steel | Alloy of aluminium with 4% copper and 1% manganese, giving greater strength than aluminium. |

| Aluminium | Good strength to weight ratio. Good conductor of heat and electricity. |

1 Choose the correct smart material from the options given to complete the table below. The terms can be used more than once.

    Solar cell   **LCD**   **Smart cable**   **Smart wire**   **Piezo transducer**
    QTC   **Optical fibre**   **Thermo-colour sheet**

Smart Material	Description
a) _____	Shortens in length when a small electrical current is passed through it.
b) _____	Changes from an insulator to a conductor of electrical current when compressed.
c) _____	Produces a small voltage when deformed and also deforms when a voltage is applied to it.
d) _____	Converts solar energy into electrical energy.
e) _____	If touched by hand, body heat causes the material to change colour.
f) _____	Carries light signals along its length and is widely used in communications, medical applications and hazardous areas.
g) _____	Made up of shaped crystals that have individual electrical connections.
h) _____	Inexpensive transducer that's made up of a thin slice of Piezo electric material bonded to a brass disc.
i) _____	Gives a better signal than conductive electrical wire.
j) _____	Has bar-shaped crystals to display numbers.
k) _____	Converts mechanical energy into electrical energy.
l) _____	Expected to revolutionise the design of switches and keyboards.
m) _____	Made from nickel and titanium.
n) _____	Has dot-shaped crystals to display letters.
o) _____	Can be used to power orbiting satellites.

Injection and Blow Moulding

Injection Moulding

1 Name four plastics that can be injection moulded.

a) ....

b) ....

c) ....

d) ....

2 The following stages describe the process of injection moulding. Number them **1–4** to put them in the correct order.

A The heater melts the plastic as the screw moves the plastic towards the mould. ⬭

B Plastic powder or granules are fed from the hopper to a steel barrel. ⬭

C When the plastic has cooled, the mould opens. ⬭

D The hydraulic system forces the plastic into the mould. ⬭

Blow Moulding

3 Name three plastics that can be blow moulded.

a) ....

b) ....

c) ....

4 The following stages describe the process of injection moulding. Number them **1–3** to put them in the correct order.

A The air expands in the tube, forcing the plastic to the sides of the mould. ⬭

B Air is blown into an extruded section of the tube. ⬭

C It is cooled, then opened to remove the product. ⬭

Vacuum Forming and Line Bending

Vacuum Forming

1 What group of plastics is used in vacuum forming?

....

2 What is the most popular plastic used in vacuum forming? Tick the correct option.

A Acrylic ⬭ **B** Nylon ⬭ **C** ABS ⬭

D GRP ⬭ **E** HIPS ⬭ **F** PVC ⬭

3 The following stages show the process of vacuum forming. Number them **1–6** to put them in the correct order.

A Lower mould and remove plastic from machine. ⬭

B Move mould upwards towards the plastic. ⬭

C Heat plastic. ⬭

D Place mould and plastic in machine. ⬭

E Remove heater, switch on vacuum pump to suck plastic onto the mould. ⬭

F Switch off vacuum pump and allow plastic to cool. ⬭

Line Bending

4 What group of plastics is used in line bending?

....

....

5 Name a plastic that can be shaped by line bending.

....

....

6 Fill in the missing words to complete the following sentence.

Bending jigs are used in line bending for the production of accurate .... and

....

7 Name a hazard when using a vacuum forming machine or line bending machine and give a suitable precaution.

Hazard: ....

Precaution: ....

PCB Design

Designing a PCB

1 Give two ways in which you can test the design of an electronic circuit.

a) *Circuit Wizard*

b) *Computer simulation*

2 What is the distance between the pin connections on an Integrated Circuit (IC)? Tick the correct option.

A 0.1 inches ✓

B 0.1 centimetres ☐

C 0.5 inches ☐

D 1 inch ☐

3 a) What can happen if you make the pads on a PCB too small? Tick the correct option.

A It can make soldering difficult ✓

B It can be damaged easily ☐

b) What can happen if you make the tracks on a PCB too narrow? Tick the correct option.

A It can make soldering difficult ✓

B It can be damaged easily ✓

4 What is the name of the etching solution used in the etching tank?

Ferric Chloride

5 What are the two sides of a PCB called?

a)

b)

Surface Mount Components

6 The two methods used for component assembly are the through hole method and the surface mount method. Which method is used most in industry?

7 Fill in the missing words to complete the following sentence.

Surface mount resistors and capacitors look like tiny .... with .... end caps.

8 What are the advantages of designing a PCB using surface mount components?

PCB Production

Photo Etch Method

1 The following stages describe the process of photo-etching. Number them **1–5** to put them in the correct order.

A Place the acetate mask in a light box with a piece of photo-resist board for 120 seconds. ◯

B Develop the photo-resist board, remove and wash in cold water. ◯

C Copy the artwork onto acetate sheet. ◯

D Place the developed board in an etching tank. ◯

E Remove and wash in cold water. ◯

2 What two health and safety checks should you take into account when making a PCB?

a) ....

b) ....

Protoboards

3 What is another name for a solderless protoboard? Tick the correct option.

A Veroboard ☑   **B** Breadboard ◯

4 When would you use a solderless protoboard?

....

5 Give an advantage of using a solderless protoboard.

....

Stripboards

6 What is another name for stripboard? Tick the correct option.

A Veroboard ◯   **B** Breadboard ☑

7 What is the difference between solderless protoboard and stripboard?

....

8 What is the advantage of using stripboard?

....

PCB Assembly

Quality Control

1 When drilling PCB pads, what size drill should you use? Tick the correct option.

    A   0.5 mm ◯   **B**   1 mm ◯   **C**   2 mm ◯   **D**   3 mm ◯

2 Give three health and safety checks you should take into account when drilling PCB pads.

    a) ....

    b) ....

    c) ....

3 What is the name of the component assembly method that doesn't require holes in PCBs?

    ....

4 Give an example of quality control when building a PCB.

    ....

5 What would you use a multimeter set on the ohms range for?

    ....

Quality Assurance

6 Give an advantage of using strain holes.

    ....

7 What is the reason for colour coding the leads of polar components in red and black sleeving?

    ....

Populating the PCB

8 The following statements show components that are to be soldered onto a PCB. Number them **1–3** to put them into the correct order of how you would assemble them.

    A   Tall components ◯   **B**   Low components ◯   **C**   Sensitive components ◯

9 How can you eliminate a dry joint when soldering?

    ....

    ....

Computer Aided Manufacture

Computer Aided Manufacture

1 a) What is Computer Aided Manufacture often referred to as?

....

b) What is Computer Aided Design often referred to as?

....

c) What kind of data does Computer Aided Manufacture rely on?

....

d) What does CNC stand for in Computer Aided Manufacture? Tick the correct option.

A Computer Numbered Control ◯   **B** Computer Numerical Centre ◯

C Computer Numerical Control ◯   **D** Computer Numbering Control ◯

2 Fill in the missing words to complete the following sentence.

Post processing is .... Code created by the .... software.

Axis Machines

3 Describe the features of the following Computer Aided Manufacturing machines.

a) Two-axis machine: ....

....

b) Three-axis machine: ....

....

c) Four-axis machine: ....

....

CO_2 Lasers and Rapid Prototyping

4 Fill in the missing words to complete the following sentences.

Laser machines can cut a wide variety of materials very ...., removing the smallest

amount of material. Rapid prototyping is used in industry to create .... ◯

prototypes.

Scales of Production

Production Methods

© Lonsdale

1 What production methods are each of the following sentences describing?

a) Component parts arrive at exactly the time the factory needs them. Less storage space is needed. If the components supply is stopped, the production line stops.

....

b) The product goes through various stages on a production line. Usually involves the product being produced for days or even weeks in large numbers. Production could be halted if a problem occurs at any stage.

....

c) One product is made at a particular time. It could be a prototype or an intricate object. It usually takes a long time, which results in an expensive product.

....

d) The product is continually produced over hours, days or even years. Often results in a relatively inexpensive product.

....

e) A series of products are made together in small or large quantities. Once made, another series of products may be produced with the same equipment and workforce.

....

Product Life Cycle

2 a) Explain why evolutionary design is more common than revolutionary design.

....

....

b) Why do products have a life cycle built into them?

....

3 Choose the correct words from the options given to identify which stage in the product life cycle is being described.

| Introduction | Growth | Maturity | Decline |

a) The car is selling well and making lots of money for the company. ....

b) The car has been designed, made, tested and finally launched. ....

c) Sales of the car have dropped and the company is making no profit. ....

d) Car sales are increasing and manufacturing is more profitable. ....

© Lonsdale

Consumer Protection and Environment

Standards and the Consumers' Association

1 a) What do the following symbols mean?

i) $C\epsilon$ ....

ii) ....

b) What do the above symbols tell consumers about the products that display them?

....

....

c) How can manufacturers get these symbols on their products?

....

....

2 Describe what *Which?* magazine does with regards to consumer advice.

....

....

....

Effects on the Environment

3 What is meant by a 'throwaway society'?

....

....

4 Give three examples of electronic products that quickly become out of date.

a) ....

b) ....

c) ....

5 Fill in the missing word to complete the following sentence.

Batteries and electronic components should be disposed of by correct ....

Electronic Circuit Symbols

Electronic Circuit Symbols

1 Complete the following table.

Electrolytic capacitor	Diode	Battery	Push to break switch
Operational amplifier	Bell	Loudspeaker	NOT gate
Microphone	Motor	LDR	Field effect transistor

Name	Symbol	Name	Symbol
Fixed Resistor		Piezo Crystal Oscillator	
a)		g)	
b)		h)	
c)		i)	
d)		j)	
e)		k)	
f)		l)	

Mechanical Switches

1 Draw the circuit symbol for the following switches.

a) Single pole double throw

b) Double pole double throw

c) Single pole single throw

a)

b)

c)

2 What's the difference between a single pole single throw switch and a single pole double throw switch?

....

3 Give two uses for a double pole double throw switch.

a) ....

b) ....

Types of Mechanical Switches

4 Name the following mechanical switches.

a)

....

b)

....

c)

....

d)

....

e)

....

f)

....

g)

....

h)

....

i)

....

j)

....

k)
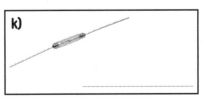
....

Batteries

Batteries

1 Why should you not use mains electricity as the energy source for your project?

Due to potential dangers.

2 Fill in the missing word to complete the following sentence.

A battery contains *electrical* energy.

3 Give two requirements you need to consider when selecting a battery for your project.

a) *the voltage type., physical size.*

b) *power requirments*

Battery Types

4 Label the batteries in the space provided. The first one has been done for you.

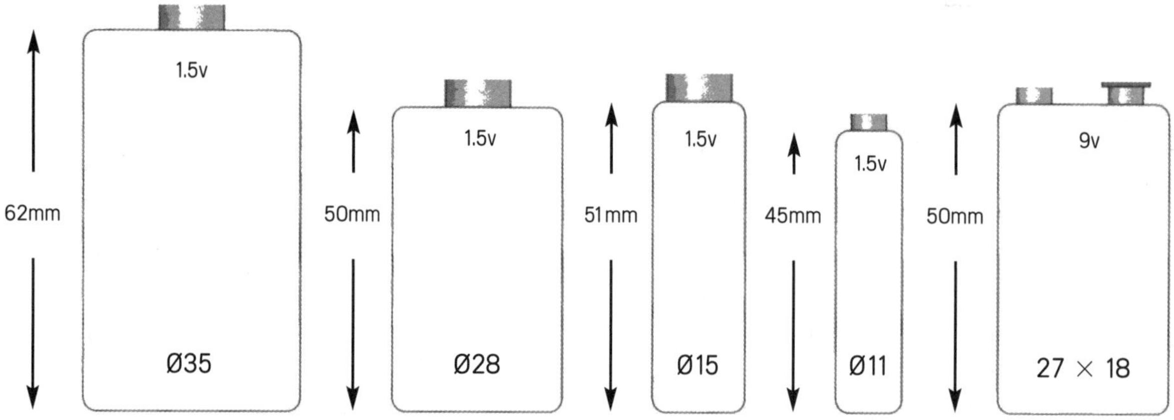

1.5v	1.5v	1.5v	1.5v	9v
62mm	50mm	51mm	45mm	50mm
Ø35	Ø28	Ø15	Ø11	27 × 18

a) D   b) *C*   c) *AA*   d) *AAA*   e) *PP3*

5 Choose the correct words from the options given to complete the sentences below.

~~Lithium~~   ~~Silver oxide~~   ~~Zinc carbon~~   ~~Nickel cadmium~~   ~~Alkaline~~

a) *Zinc carbon.* is the most basic battery.

b) *Alkaline* batteries give longer life than zinc carbon.

c) *Silver oxide.* button cells are used in watches, clocks and cameras.

d) *Lithium* cells are expensive with a very long life.

e) *Nickel cadmium* batteries are rechargeable and available in most sizes.

well done ✓

Resistors

1 Give two uses for a resistor in an electronic circuit.

a) *Limits the amount current flowing*

b) *Set voltage levels in certain parts of the circuit*

The Ohm

2 Rewrite the following resistances using the multipliers R, K and M.

a) 150 Ohms   *1ᴺ50k*

b) 1800 Ohms   *1k8*

c) 3.3 Ohms   *3R3k*

d) 12 000 000 Ohms   *12M*

e) 5 600 Ohms   *5k86*

f) 10 Ohms

g) 82 000 000 Ohms   *82M*

h) 47 Ohms

i) 3 300 Ohms   *3k3*

j) 7.5 Ohms   *7k5*

The Resistor Colour Code

3 Complete the following table by working out the value and tolerance of the resistors. You are given the four colours of the bands on the resistors.

Band 1	Band 2	Band 3	Band 4	Resistor Value and Tolerance
brown 1	green 5	red 00 2	gold	a) 1500 ±5%
red 2	red 2	yellow 0000	silver	b) 220000 ±10%
yellow 4	violet 7	black	silver	c) 47 ±10%
green 5	blue 6	blue 000 000	gold	d) 56000000 ±5%
violet 7	green 5	orange 000	gold	e) 75000. ±5%

Resistors

Preferred Values

1 Why are resistors produced with a certain number of preferred values to a particular tolerance?

_____

2 Complete the following table by selecting resistors from the E12 and E24 series.

	Resistor Value	Tolerance	Band 1	Band 2	Band 3	Band 4
a)	560 +-10%	±10%	green	**b)** blue	brown	**c)** silver
d) 33000 +-10%		±10%	**e)** orange	orange	yellow	**f)** silver
g) 7500 +-5%		±5%	violet	**h)** green	red	**i)** gold
j)			blue	**k)**	red	silver
l)			**m)**	yellow	orange	gold

3 Give two differences between the resistors from the E12 series and those from the E24 series.

a) _____

b) _____

Other Types of Resistor

4 Draw lines between the boxes to match the type of resistor to its circuit symbol and what it looks like.

Preset variable resistor	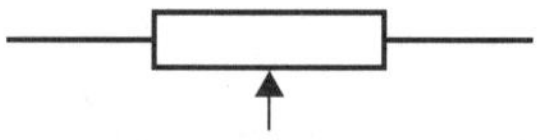	
Rotary potentiometer	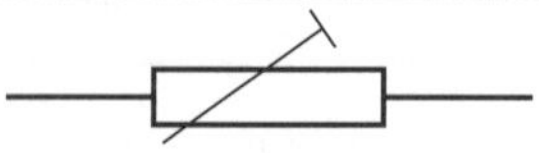	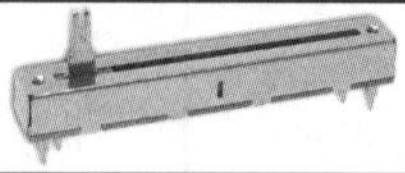
Slide variable resistor	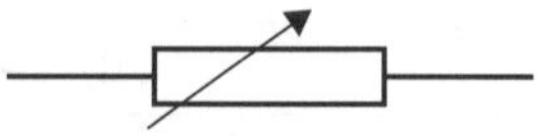	

Current Limiting Resistors

5 a) What is the purpose of using a current-limiting resistor in a circuit?

_____

b) Give two components that are protected by using a current-limiting resistor.

i) _____ **ii)** _____

Ohm's Law

1 Which of the following represent the correct formula for the relationship between current, voltage and resistance? Tick the correct options.

A voltage = current ÷ resistance ◯

B voltage = resistance ÷ current ◯ ✓

C voltage = current × resistance ☑ ✓

D current = voltage ÷ resistance ☑ ✓

E current = resistance ÷ voltage ◯

F current = voltage × resistance ◯

G resistance = current ÷ voltage ☑ ✓

H resistance = voltage ÷ current ◯

I resistance = current × voltage ◯

2 a) What current passes through a 12R resistor if the voltage across it is 6 volts? $6v ÷ 12r = 2I$

Formula: $\frac{V}{R} = I$ ~~6v ÷ 12R~~ = ~~12r ÷ 6v~~

Working: $6v ÷ 12r = ~~2I~~$ $0.5I$

Answer with units: $2I$

b) What current passes through a 2K resistor if the voltage across it is 9 volts?

$I = \frac{V}{R}$

Formula: 2000

Working: $I = 9/2000$

Answer with units: $I = 0.0045$ amps

c) A current of 4mA passes through a 2K resistor. What is the voltage across the resistor?

Formula: ~~V = 4 × 2000 = 8000~~ $V = I × R$

Working: $V = \overset{0.004}{4} × 2000 = 8v$

Answer with units: ~~8~~ $V = 8$ $8v$

d) Calculate the resistance of a resistor if a current of 3mA passes through it when the voltage across it is 9 volts.

Formula: $R = \frac{V}{I}$

Working: $0.003 × 9v$

Answer with units: $R = 0.027$

◻

Resistors in Series

1 Calculate the total resistance of the following resistors connected in series.

a)

R₁ — 750R   R₂ — 150R

Formula: $R_{total} = R_1 + R_2$

Working: $R_{total} = 750R + 150R$

Answer with units: **900R**

b)

R₁ — 2K2   R₂ — 2K   R₃ — 20K

Formula: $R_{total} = R_1 + R_2 + R_3$

Working: $R_{total} = 2K2 + 2K + 20K$

Answer with units: **24K2**

2 When two or more resistors are connected in series, the same amount of electrical current passes through each resistor. In the following combination, a current of 1.5mA passes through each resistor.

OHM LAW
$V = I \times R$
$I = V/R$
$R = V/I$

R₁ — 1K / 1000   R₂ — 2K / 2000   R₃ — 3K / 3000

$\dfrac{1.5}{1000} = 0.0015$

a) Calculate the voltage across:

i) resistor R1

0.0015×1000.

Formula: $V = I \times R$ Working: 0.0015×1000.   Answer with units: **1.5v**.

ii) resistor R2

Formula: $V = I \times R$ Working: 0.0015×2000 Answer with units: **3.0v**.

iii) resistor R3

Formula: $V = I \times R$ Working: 0.0015×3000 Answer with units: **4.5v**

b) What is the total voltage across the combination of resistors above?

9v

Resistors in Parallel

1 Calculate the total resistance of the following resistors connected in parallel.

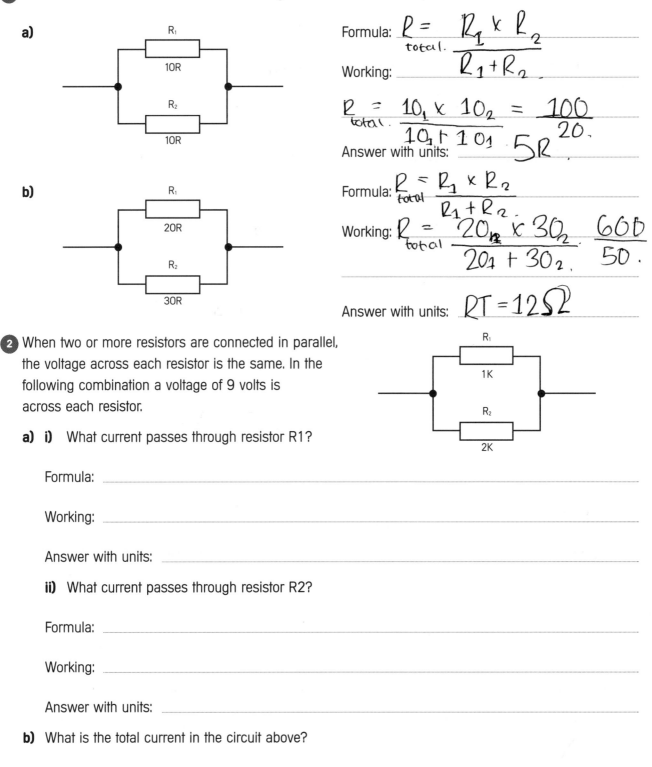

a)

R₁
10R

R₂
10R

Formula: $R_{total} = \dfrac{R_1 \times R_2}{R_1 + R_2}$

Working:

$$R_{total} = \dfrac{10_1 \times 10_2}{10_1 + 10_1} = \dfrac{100}{20}$$

Answer with units: $5R$

b)

R₁
20R

R₂
30R

Formula: $R_{total} = \dfrac{R_1 \times R_2}{R_1 + R_2}$

Working: $R_{total} = \dfrac{20_{12} \times 30_2}{20_1 + 30_2} \quad \dfrac{600}{50}$

Answer with units: $RT = 12\,\Omega$

2 When two or more resistors are connected in parallel, the voltage across each resistor is the same. In the following combination a voltage of 9 volts is across each resistor.

R₁
1K

R₂
2K

a) i) What current passes through resistor R1?

Formula:

Working:

Answer with units:

ii) What current passes through resistor R2?

Formula:

Working:

Answer with units:

b) What is the total current in the circuit above?

Potential Dividers

© Lonsdale

1 Calculate the voltage, Vout, for each of the following potential dividers.

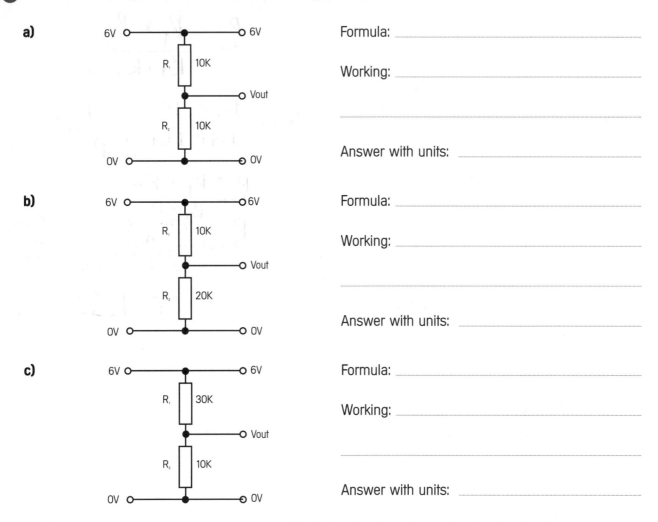

a)

Formula: ....

Working: ....

....

Answer with units: ....

b)

Formula: ....

Working: ....

....

Answer with units: ....

c)

Formula: ....

Working: ....

....

Answer with units: ....

2 **a)** When the voltage supply to a potential divider is 9 volts, the voltage, Vout, is 6 volts. Choose two suitable resistor values from the E24 series for R1 and R2 for the potential divider. Explain your choice.

....

....

....

b) Choose two suitable resistor values from the E24 series for R1 and R2 if the voltage, Vout, is a quarter of the voltage supply in a potential divider. Explain your choice.

....

....

LDRs and Thermistors

1 Fill in the missing words to complete the following sentences.

a) LDRs and thermistors are used to give a .... resistance.

b) LDRs and thermistors are used in series with a .... resistor to set a switching level.

c) An LDR converts changes in .... into changes in electrical current.

d) A thermistor converts changes in .... into changes in electrical current.

e) The resistance of a .... co-efficient thermistor decreases as it gets hotter.

2 What is the advantage of including a variable resistor, rather than a fixed resistor of known size, in a potential divider that includes an LDR or a thermistor?

....

....

3 The diagram shows an LDR as part of a potential divider. Explain what happens to the voltage, Vout, when the light intensity on the LDR increases.

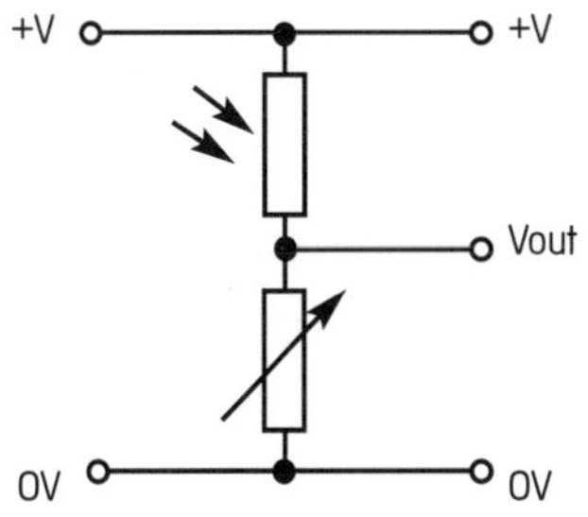

a) ....

....

....

b) Sketch in the box what an LDR looks like.

Resistor Power Ratings

Resistor Power Ratings

1 Which of the following represent the correct formulae for the relationship between power, voltage and current? Tick the correct options.

A power = voltage ÷ current ◯   **B** power = current ÷ voltage ◯

C power = voltage × current ◯   **D** voltage = power ÷ current ◯

E voltage = current ÷ power ◯   **F** voltage = power × current ◯

G current = power ÷ voltage ◯   **H** current = voltage ÷ power ◯

I current = power × voltage ◯

2 a) A resistor has a voltage of 6 volts across it. Calculate its resistance and choose a suitable resistor from the E24 series if the maximum current that passes through the resistor is 15mA.

Formula: ....

Working: ....

Answer with units: ....   Chosen resistor: ....

b) Calculate the power rating of the resistor.

Formula: ....

Working: ....

Answer with units: ....

3 A current-limiting resistor in series with an LED is needed to allow a maximum current of 20mA to pass through the LED. The total voltage across the resistor and LED is 6 volts, of which 2 volts are across the LED.

Calculate the resistance of the current-limiting resistor and choose a suitable resistor from the E24 series.

Formula: ....

Working: ....

Answer with units: ....   Chosen resistor: ....

Capacitors

1 What do capacitors store in electronic circuits?

electrical charge.

2 Give two uses for capacitors in electronic circuits.

a) *Monostable*

b) *Control the frequency of pulse generators*

3 What is displayed on the case of a capacitor? Tick the correct options.

A Capacitor size ☐   B Time constant ☑

C Discharge rate ☐   D Working voltage ☑

4 Give three units of capacitance (apart from the Farad) that most capacitors are measured in. For each unit, state how its value relates to the Farad.

a) i) Unit of capacitance: *Micro*   ii) How value relates to the Farad:

b) i) Unit of capacitance: *Nano*   ii) How value relates to the Farad:

c) i) Unit of capacitance: *Pico*   ii) How value relates to the Farad:

Charging and Discharging Capacitors

5 Calculate the time constant of the following capacitor and resistor combinations.

a)

```
——————o 9V
  |
 [1M]
  |
+ ═╪═  1µF
  |
——————o 0V
```

Formula:

Working:

Answer with units:

b)

```
——————o 9V
  |
 [100K]
  |
+ ═╪═  47µF
  |
——————o 0V
```

Formula: *T = C × R*

Working: *T = 47 × 100R*

Answer with units: *470*

Capacitors

Charging and Discharging Capacitors (cont.)

1 The graph shows the voltage across a capacitor that is being charged through a resistor.

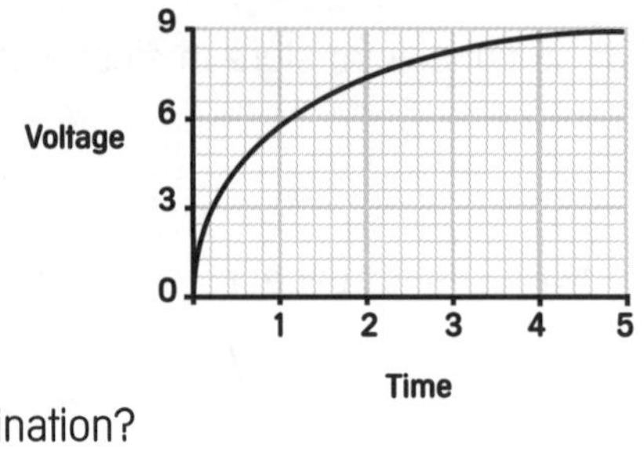

Voltage vs Time graph with Voltage axis marked 0, 3, 6, 9 and Time axis marked 1, 2, 3, 4, 5.

a) What is the time constant of the capacitor and resistor combination?

....

....

b) Explain your answer to part a).

....

....

....

Types of Capacitors

2 Why are electrolytic capacitors only manufactured in multiples of 1, 2.2 and 4.7?

....

....

3 a) Draw the circuit symbols for an electrolytic capacitor and a non-electrolytic capacitor in the boxes below.

i) Electrolytic	**ii)** Non-electrolytic

4 Give three differences between electrolytic capacitors and non-electrolytic capacitors.

a) ....

b) ....

c) ....

Types of Capacitors (cont.)

1 Draw a radial and an axial electrolytic capacitor in the boxes below. Label the leads of the capacitors to show polarity.

a) Radial

b) Axial

Capacitors in Series

2 Calculate the total capacitance of the following combinations of capacitors.

a)

10µF   10µF

Formula: ....

Working: ....

....

Answer with units: ....

b)

1µF   1µF

Formula: ....

Working: ....

....

Answer with units: ....

c)

22µF   22µF

Formula: ....

Working: ....

....

Answer with units: ....

d)

10µF   22µF

Formula: ....

Working: ....

....

Answer with units: ....

Capacitors in Parallel

Capacitors in Series (cont.)

1. A student needs a capacitor with a value of 20μF and decides to connect two 10μF capacitors in series. Without any calculations, explain why this combination is wrong.

Capacitors in Parallel

2. Calculate the total capacitance of the following combinations of capacitors.

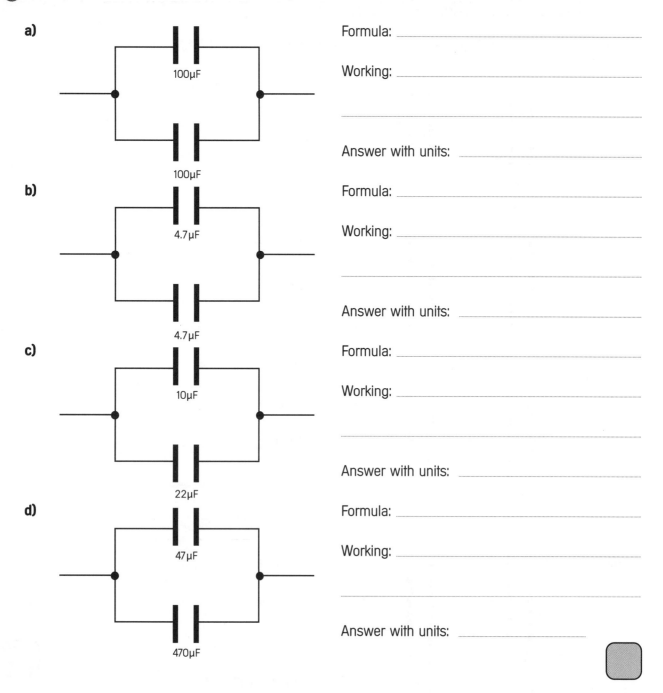

a)

100μF

100μF

Formula:

Working:

Answer with units:

b)

4.7μF

4.7μF

Formula:

Working:

Answer with units:

c)

10μF

22μF

Formula:

Working:

Answer with units:

d)

47μF

470μF

Formula:

Working:

Answer with units:

Diodes

Diodes

1 a) What is a diode?

....

....

b) i) Draw the circuit symbol for a diode and label the anode and cathode.

ii) Sketch what the diode looks like and label the anode and cathode.

How Diodes Work

2 a) Complete the following diagram by including a diode so that the lamp stays off when the switch is closed.

b) Complete the following diagram by including a diode so that the lamp comes on when the switch is closed.

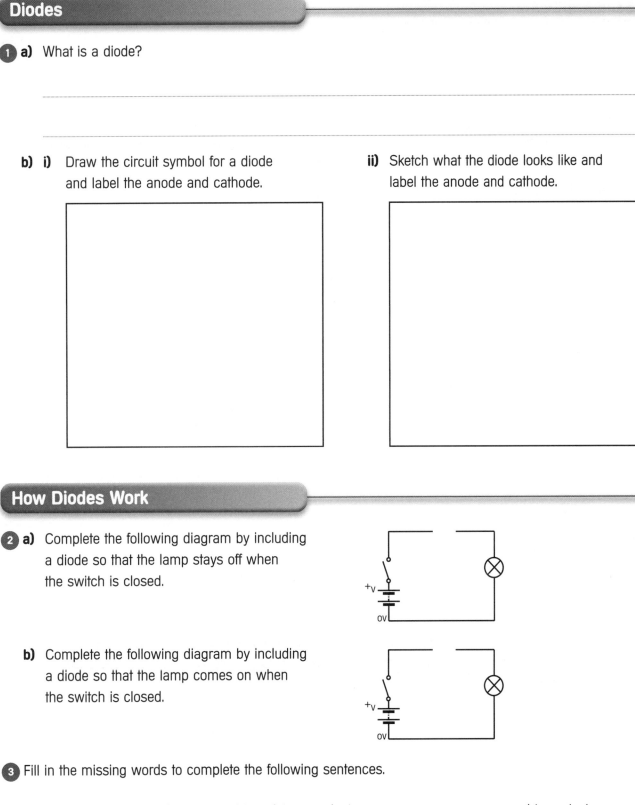

3 Fill in the missing words to complete the following sentences.

Diodes are used in circuits to protect transistors against .... and to protect

components against .... battery ....

Light Emitting Diodes

Light Emitting Diodes

1 **a)** What is a light emitting diode?

....

b) **i)** Draw the circuit symbol for a light emitting diode and label the anode and cathode.

ii) Sketch what the light emitting diode looks like and label the anode, cathode and flat.

2 When using an LED in a circuit, why should you always include a resistor in series with it?

....

3 **a)** **i)** A resistor is used in series with an LED. The LED needs a voltage of about 2 volts to make it work. The total voltage across the resistor and LED is 9 volts. Calculate the resistance of the resistor if a maximum current of 20mA is to pass through the LED.

Formula: ....

Working: ....

Answer with units: ....

ii) Choose a suitable resistor from the E12 series and explain why you chose it.

Chosen resistor: ....

b) **i)** A resistor is used in series with an LED. The LED needs a voltage of about 2 volts to make it work. The total voltage across the resistor and LED is 12 volts. Calculate the resistance of the resistor if a maximum current of 20mA is to pass through the LED.

Formula: ....

Working: ....

Answer with units: ....

ii) Choose a suitable resistor from the E24 series and explain why you chose it.

....

Steering Diodes

1 The diagram shows a 4017 IC decade counter with its outputs driving six LEDs. The LEDs light up in the sequence 1, 2, 3, 4, 5, 6, 5, 4, 3, 2, etc. The circuit includes eight steering diodes in order for the LEDs to light in this sequence.

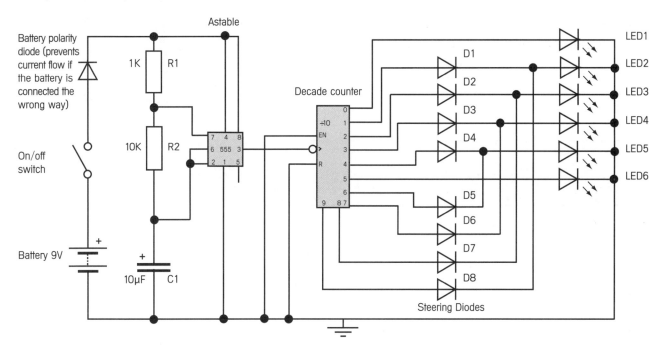

Complete the following table to show what happens in order to get the above sequence of LEDs. The first two have been done for you.

Decade Counter Pin	LED that Lights Up	Diode that is Forward Biased	Diode that is Reverse Biased
0	LED 1	NONE	NONE
1	LED 2	D1	D8
2			
3			
4			
5			
6			
7			
8			
9			

Seven-segment Display

1 A seven-segment LED display can be used to show numbers from 0 to 9. Each segment location is given a specific letter (a to g) as shown in the diagram.

Complete the table by ticking which segments need to be lit in order to produce each number. The first one has been done for you.

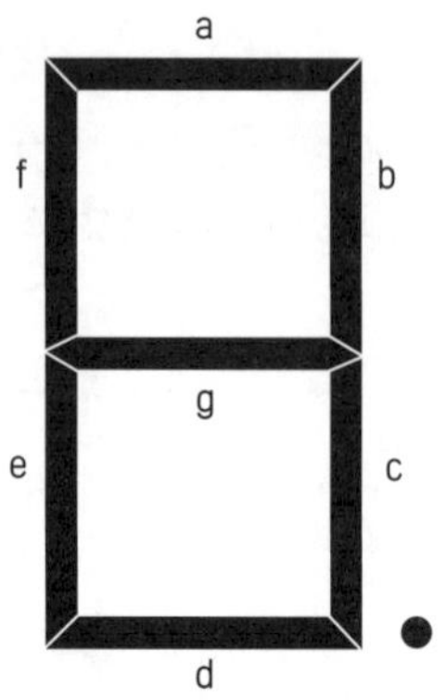

Number Provided	Segment Lit						
	a	b	c	d	e	f	g
0	✔	✔	✔	✔	✔	✔	
1							
2							
3							
4							
5							
6							
7							
8							
9							

2 Choose the correct term from the options given to complete the sentence below.

cathode leads   **anode leads**

A common cathode seven-segment display has all the .... connected to the OV rail.

3 Describe what will happen if a single current-limiting resistor is used to connect the common cathode to the OV rail.

....

....

Transistors

1 Fill in the missing words to complete the following sentences.

Transistors are used as _current_ amplifiers and as _electronic_ switches.

There are two types of transistor – bipolar and _field_ effect.

Bipolar Transistors

2 In the boxes provided, draw the circuit symbols for an npn transistor and a pnp transistor. For each symbol, label the leads.

a) npn transistor
collecter.
Base
emitter.

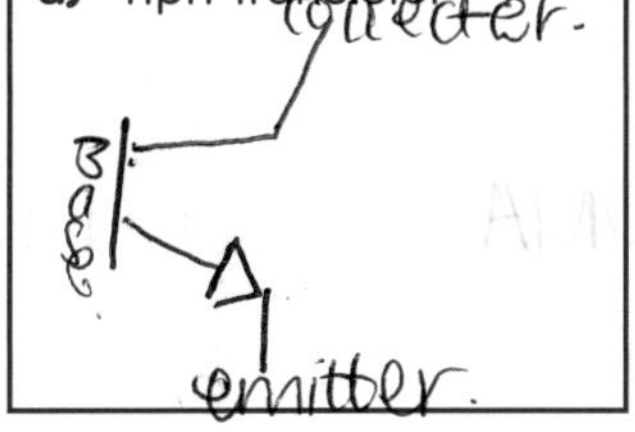

b) pnp transistor
collecror.
Base
Emitter

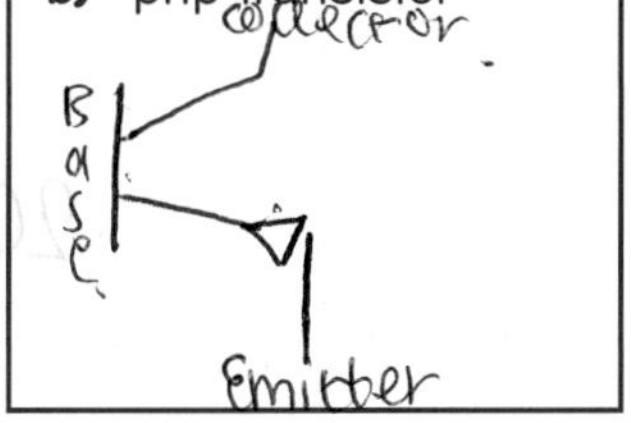

3 What's the difference between an npn transistor and a pnp transistor?

difference between them is the direction of current.

4 Are the following statements about bipolar transistors **true** or **false**?

a) The leads of a transistor are called the base, collector and emitter. _true_

b) A bipolar transistor is controlled by applying a voltage of more than 0.7 volts to its collector.

true

c) There is low resistance between the collector and emitter when a transistor is switched off.

false

d) A bipolar transistor is an analogue device. _true_

e) A transistor allows a large current to flow from the collector to the emitter as the base current

increases. _true_

f) A transistor is fully switched off if there is a voltage of about 1.5 volts between the base and

emitter. _false_

g) Transistors are made from semi-conductor material. _true_

Transistor Calculations

Transistor Calculations

1 What does 'gain' mean when it is used in connection with transistors?

Divide the collector currents by the base currents.

2 **a)** Calculate the gain of a BC548 transistor if the collector current is 80mA when the base current is 0.4mA.

Formula: $hFE = \dfrac{I_c}{I_b}$

Working: $= \dfrac{80\,mA}{0.$4$mA}$

Answer: $200MA$

b) Calculate the gain of a BC639 transistor if the collector current is 120mA and the base current is 3mA.

Formula: $hFE = \dfrac{I_c}{I_b}$

Working: $= \dfrac{120\,MA}{3MA}$

Answer: $40\,NA$

3 The hFE gain of a BC548 is 225 when the collector current is 90mA. Calculate the base current.

Formula: $hFE \times I_c = I_b$

Working: $225 \times 90\,MA$

Answer with units: $20\,250$

4 When the base current of a BC639 transistor is 3.5mA its hFE gain is 40. Calculate the collector current.

Formula:

Working:

Answer with units:

Darlington Pair Transistors

1 The circuit shows a BC548 transistor being used to switch on an LED.

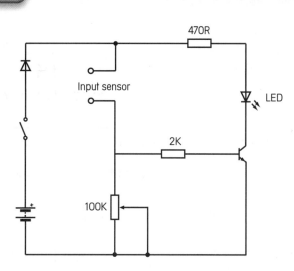

470R

LED

2K

100K

Input sensor

a) What is the purpose of the diode in series with the 9 volt power supply?

the diode stops the current from flowing to the battery is on the other way.

b) What is the purpose of the 2K resistor that is connected to the base of the transistor?

c) What is the purpose of the 470R resistor that is connected in series with the LED?

current limiting resistor LED.

d) What is the purpose of the 100K potentiometer?

forms a potential divider.

2 a) Give two input devices that could be used as an input sensor.

i) _____ **ii)** _____

b) If the gain of a BC548 transistor is 220 and the gain of a BC639 transistor is 40, calculate the gain of the Darlington driver.

Diode

Input sensor

On/Off switch

Output

Buzzer

2K

BC548

BC639

100K

9V

Working: _____

_____

Answer: _____

Field Effect Transistors

1 a) Draw the symbol for a Field Effect Transistor (FET) and label each lead.

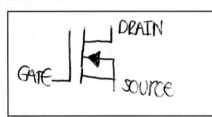

b) Choose the correct words from the options given to complete the sentences below.

| **output** | **input signal** | **OV** |

i) The drain is connected to _Input Signal_.

ii) The gate is connected to _output_.

iii) The source is connected to _0 v_.

2 Circle the correct options in the following sentences.

a) A FET switches on when voltage is **greater than** / **less than** 2V on the gate.

b) A FET switches off when voltage is **greater than** / **less than** 2V on the gate.

3 Fill in the missing words to complete the following sentences.

A FET is an example of a _digital_ switching device. Once the gate is

above 2v, it fully switches on immediately.

4 Why are logic ICs and PICs often interfaced with FETs in electronic circuits?

Because very little current is used
and it accepts amplifies the voltage.

5 The circuit shows a FET being used to switch on a motor.

a) Explain why the motor is switched on when the touch contacts are bridged with a finger.

+V ○
Diode ⟁ (M)
Touch Contacts
Drain
Source
Gate
OV ○

_____

_____

b) What is the purpose of the reverse-biased diode across the motor?

_____

Thyristors

1 a) Draw the circuit symbol for a thyristor and label each lead.

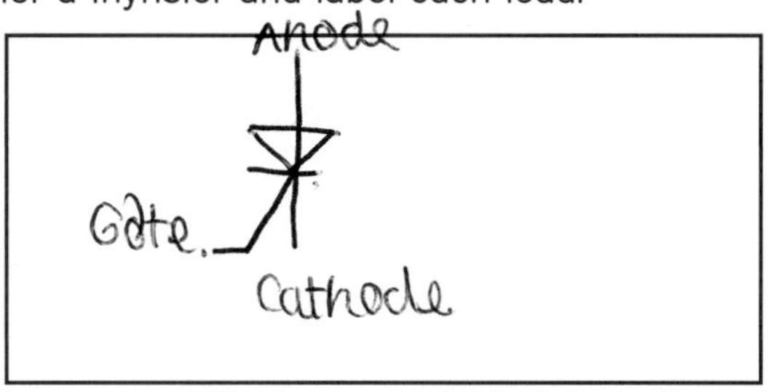

Anode

Gate.

Cathode

b) Choose the correct words from the options given to complete the sentences below.

output   **input signal**   **0V**

i) The gate is connected to _out put_ .

ii) The anode is connected to _input signal_ .

iii) The cathode is connected to _0V_ .

2 Choose the correct word from the options given to complete the sentence below.

astable   **monostable**   **bistable**

A thyristor is an example of a(n) _bistable_ electronic device.

3 a) When does a thyristor allow a current to flow from its anode to its cathode?

when the voltage is above 2vs

b) A thyristor is an example of an electronic latch. Explain what this means.

c) Explain how a thyristor is reset once it has been switched on.

4 What colour insulation would you use to colour code the leads of a thyristor?

a) Anode: _Red_

b) Gate: _blue_

c) Cathode: _black_

Using Thyristors

Using Thyristors in Circuits

1 The circuit shows a thyristor being used to switch a buzzer on and off.

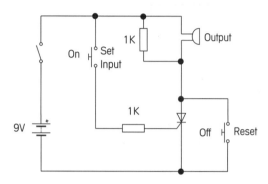

a) Explain why the buzzer is switched on when the Set switch is pressed.

....

b) What happens to the buzzer when the Reset switch is pressed?

....

c) What is the purpose of the 1K resistor in parallel with the buzzer?

....

....

2 a) Complete the following diagram. Add a 100K resistor and touch contacts so that the buzzer is switched on when the touch contacts are bridged with a finger.

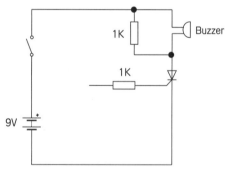

b) Suggest a material that could be used to make the touch contacts.

....

Relays and Solenoids

Relays

1 a) Are the following statements **true** or **false**?

    i) Relays are used to connect two circuits together by magnetism. ....

    ii) Relays are used to create a latch. ....

    iii) Relays are used to reduce power to a circuit. ....

b) List three disadvantages of using a relay in a circuit.

    i) ....

    ii) ....

    iii) ....

2 The following diagram shows the parts of a relay. Match parts **A–I** with the labels **1–9** on the diagram. Enter the appropriate number in the boxes provided.

    A Coil   ☐ (2)

    B Pivot   ☐

    C Soft iron core   ☐

    D Coil connection   ☐

    E Insulation   ☐

    F Soft iron armature   ☐

    G Springy metal   ☐

    H Switch contacts   ☐

    I Connections to external circuit   ☐

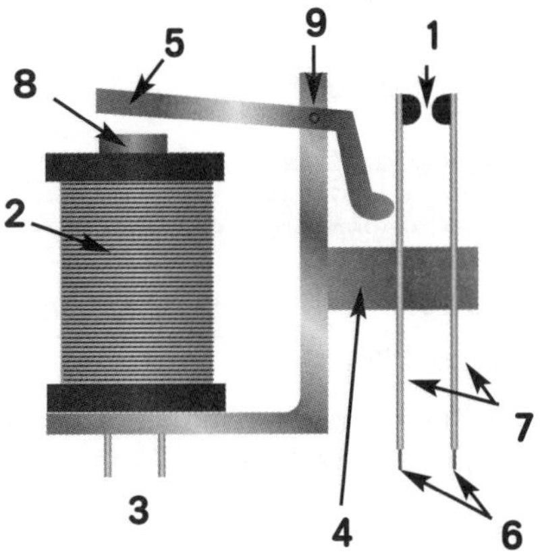

Solenoids

3 Choose the correct words from the options given to complete the sentences below.

plunger   **tube**   **coil**   **wire**   **electromagnetic**   **magnetic current**   **electrical current**

A solenoid is an .... device. When an .... is passed through the

.... it becomes magnetic and pulls the .... into the tube.

Relay Interfacing

1 The circuit shows a single pole double throw relay being used to interface a 5V control circuit to a 24V output circuit.

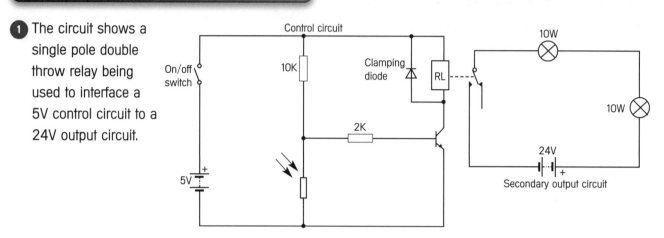

The output circuit is switched on in darkness. Fill in the missing words to complete the following sentences.

a) In darkness, the LDR has high ....

b) The base emitter voltage is taken above .... V.

c) The transistor switches .... and current flows through the relay coil.

d) Electromagnetism pulls the .... together.

Double Pole Double Throw Relay

2 The circuit shows a double pole double throw relay being used as a latch.

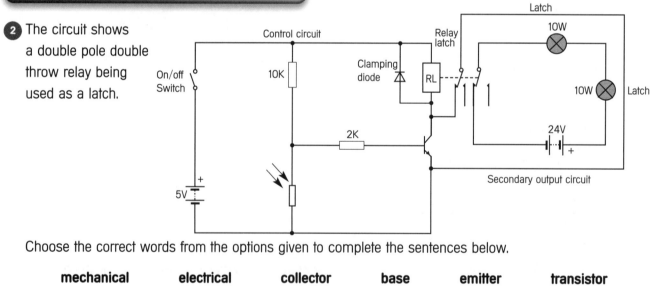

Choose the correct words from the options given to complete the sentences below.

mechanical   **electrical**   **collector**   **base**   **emitter**   **transistor**

The above latching circuit works by the extra pole and contacts providing an ....

connection across the .... and the ...., creating

a latch. When the .... switches off, the relay is latched.

Low Voltage d.c. Motors

Low Voltage d.c. Motors

1 Fill in the missing words to complete the following sentences.

a) Small d.c. motors are often called _____ motors and are cheap to buy.

b) An advantage of a d.c. motor is that it can move in a _____ direction and a

_____ direction.

c) Reversing the _____ flow through the _____ of a

d.c. motor changes the direction of rotation.

d) Connecting a d.c. motor to a _____ provides greater control of speed, direction

and torque.

2 Fill in the missing words to complete the following sentences.

a) Stepper motors are a special type of d.c. motor that can be driven in either _____

or _____ direction by small, accurate steps.

b) A PIC _____ can be used to provide the pattern of pulse for the stepper motor.

c) Each pulse to a stepper motor is equal to _____ degrees and

_____ steps are needed for one revolution.

3 Give two disadvantages of a solar motor.

a) _____

b) _____

d.c. Motor Circuits

4 Describe how electrical noise can be reduced when using a cheap d.c. motor.

_____

_____

Darlington Driver ICs

Darlington Driver ICs

1 The BC548 and the BC639 can be used to make a Darlington Driver pair.

a) What is the gain of a BC548? ....

b) What is the gain of a BC639? ....

c) What is the total gain of the two transistors? ....

d) What is the maximum current of a BC548? ....

e) What is the maximum current of a BC639? ....

f) How many transistors are contained in a BCX38 Darlington transistor? ....

g) How many Darlington transistors are contained in a ULN2003 IC? ....

h) How many Darlington transistors are contained in a ULN2803 IC? ....

2 Give three advantages of using a Darlington Driver IC to replace single transistors.

a) ....

b) ....

c) ....

Motor Driver ICs

3 How many motors can be controlled using a 16-pin motor Driver IC? Tick the correct options.

A One ⬜   **B** Two ⬜   **C** Three ⬜   **D** Four ⬜

4 Using a motor driver IC, how can the direction of a motor be changed?

....

5 Circle the correct option in the following sentence.

In a Darlington Driver IC, the suppression diodes are protecting the **transistors / motor**.

6 Give three devices that cause back emf when working.

a) ....

b) ....

c) ....

Buzzers

1 Fill in the missing words to complete the following sentences.

a) Buzzers are _____ components that change _____ energy into sound.

b) Buzzers are available with _____ leads or with pins for _____ mounting.

Piezo Transducers

2 Choose the correct words from the options given to complete the sentences below.

mechanical   **buzzers**   **electrical**   **voltage**   **sounds**   **input**   **output**

a) Piezo transducers change _____ energy into _____ energy and vice versa.

b) Piezo transducers can produce many different _____, unlike

_____, which only produce a single tone.

c) Piezo transducers can be used as an _____ device and also as an

_____ device.

Loudspeakers

3 Choose the correct words from the options given to complete the sentences below.

mechanical   **electromagnet**   **electromagnetism**   **physical**
coil   **electrical**   **chemical**   **attracts**   **repels**

a) Loudspeakers change _____ energy into _____ energy.

b) A loudspeaker works by _____.

c) When electrical current is passed through the _____ of a loudspeaker it turns

into an _____.

d) As current flows through the coil it _____ or _____ the permanent magnet.

555 IC

Integrated Circuits

1 Briefly explain what an integrated circuit is and what it consists of.

....

....

2 Most ICs are available as a Dual In Line (DIL) package. Explain what this means.

....

....

....

3 a) Fill in the missing words to complete the following sentence.

When assembling an IC on a Printed Circuit Board (PCB), using an IC socket protects the IC from

damage caused by .... and allows the IC to be easily ....

b) What is the purpose of the small notch on top of an IC?

....

4 a) Give one use for a 555 IC in a monostable circuit.

....

b) Give one use for a 555 IC in an astable circuit.

....

5 Label the following diagram of the 555 IC:

    a) Pin 1

    b) Pin 4

    c) Pin 8

    d) Indicate how Pin 1 is identified.

555 IC Monostable

555 IC Monostable

1 The pin diagram for a 555 IC is shown below. Match **A–H** with the labels **1–8** on the diagram. Enter the appropriate number in the boxes provided.

A Output ◯

B Discharge ◯

C Trigger ◯

D +Vs (3V–15V) ◯

E 0V ◯

F Control ◯

G Reset ◯

H Threshold ◯

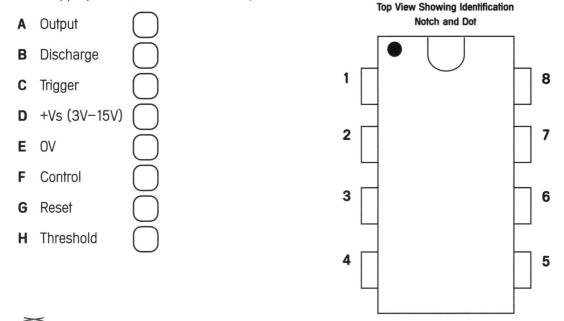

Top View Showing Identification Notch and Dot

2 **a)** Circle the correct options in the following sentences.

   i) When the voltage at output (pin 3) is high it is a **stable state / timed state**.

   ii) When the voltage at output (pin 3) is low it is a **stable state / timed state**.

b) Explain why the output voltage at pin 3 when high is only 7 volts, even though a 9-volt battery is used to power the circuit.

....

....

c) Current flows in and out of pin 3. Fill in the missing words to complete the following sentences.

   i) Pin 3 goes .... and sources current.

   ii) Pin 3 goes .... and sinks current.

555 IC Monostable

© Lonsdale

1 The circuit below shows a 555 IC being used as a monostable.

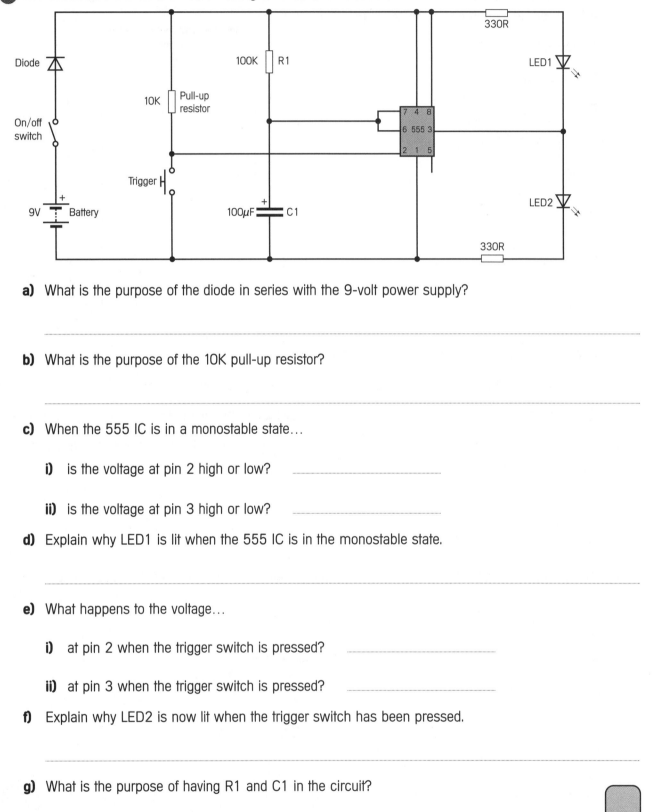

a) What is the purpose of the diode in series with the 9-volt power supply?

....

b) What is the purpose of the 10K pull-up resistor?

....

c) When the 555 IC is in a monostable state...

   i)   is the voltage at pin 2 high or low? ....

   ii) is the voltage at pin 3 high or low? ....

d) Explain why LED1 is lit when the 555 IC is in the monostable state.

....

e) What happens to the voltage...

   i)   at pin 2 when the trigger switch is pressed? ....

   ii) at pin 3 when the trigger switch is pressed? ....

f) Explain why LED2 is now lit when the trigger switch has been pressed.

....

g) What is the purpose of having R1 and C1 in the circuit?

....

Collins Revision

GCSE
D&T Electronic
Products
ESSENTIALS

Formerly
LONSDALE

Page 4

1. **a)–b) In any order:** Thermoplastics; Thermosetting plastics

2. **a)–c) Any three from:** Electrical insulator; Many colours available; Thermal insulator; Easily shaped and formed; Weather resistant; Easily injected, blown and formed; Chemical resistant; Easily fabricated; Corrosion resistant; Self-lubricating; Heat resistant; Impact resistant

3. **a)** Acrylic **b)** Nylon **c)** GRP **d)** PVC **e)** ABS **f)** HIPS **g)** Epoxy resin

Page 5

1. **a)–c) In any order: Softwoods** – Pine
   Hardwoods – Beech, Oak, Mahogany
   Manufactured Boards – Plywood, MDF

2. **a)** How easy the timber is to work.
   b) Different timber surfaces.
   c) Patterns caused by growth rings.

3. **MDF** – Widely used in furniture for bedrooms and kitchens. Useful for creating moulds for vacuum forming Made by bonding wood fibres with resin-based adhesive.
   Plywood – Constructed from an odd number of thin layers glued together. Has a uniform strength throughout. Stronger when it has a greater number of layers.
   Hardwoods – Include mahogany and beech.
   Pine – The most widely used timber for general purpose work. Can be nailed without splitting the wood and joined with screws and PVA glue.

Page 6

1. **a)** don't contain; aren't
   b) contain; are

2. **a)** The ability to retain strength when stretched.
   b) The ability to be stretched without breaking.

3. A2; B1; C3

4. **Duralumin** – Alloy of aluminium with 4% copper and 1% manganese, giving greater strength than aluminium.
   Brass – Alloy of copper with 35% zinc.
   Copper – Malleable and ductile. Excellent resistance to corrosion.
   Mild steel – Can be joined by soldering, brazing, welding. Used for general purpose engineering parts. Can be case hardened, giving a soft core and hardened outer layer. Poor resistance to corrosion.
   Aluminium – Good strength to weight ratio. Good conductor of heat and electricity.

Page 7

1. **a)** Smart wire **b)** QTC **c)** Piezo transducer
   d) Solar cell **e)** Thermo-colour sheet **f)** Optical fibre
   g) LCD **h)** Piezo transducer **i)** Optical fibre **j)** LCD
   k) Smart cable **l)** QTC **m)** Smart wire **n)** LCD
   o) Solar cell

Page 8

1. **a)–d) Any four suitable answers, for example:** Polythene; Polystyrene; Polypropylene; Nylon

2. A2; B1; C4; D3

3. **a)–c) Any three suitable answers, for example:** PVC; Polythene; Polypropylene

4. A2; B1; C3

Page 9

1. Thermoplastics

2. E

3. A6; B3; C2; D1; E4; F5

4. Thermoplastics

5. Acrylic

6. angles; shapes

7. **Any suitable examples, e.g. Hazard**: Burns from line bending machine or when plastic is being shaped. **Precaution**: Wear protective gloves; Keep fingers away from hot areas.

Page 10

1. **a)–b) In any order:** Computer simulation; Use a prototyping board.

2. A

3. **a)** A
   b) B

4. Ferric chloride

5. **a)–b) In any order:** Component side; Track side.

6. Surface mount method

7. bricks; metal

8. Smaller and cheaper PCBs with no holes to drill.

Page 11

1. A2; B3; C1; D4; E5

2. **a)–b) In any order:** Wear goggles, gloves and apron; Work in a well-ventilated place. When light box on, keep lid closed.

3. B

4. To quickly develop circuits.

5. **Any one from:** Cheap to buy; They use real components; Circuits can be quickly put together.

6. A

7. Components are pushed into protoboards. Components are soldered into stripboards.

8. It is a simple form of PCB.

Page 12

1. B

2. **a)–c) Any three suitable answers, for example:** Wear goggles; Tuck ties into shirts; Tie long hair back; Remove rings and jewellery

3. Surface mount.

4. Using a magnifying glass to inspect PCBs for breaks in tracks and missing pads.

5. Checking continuity and the size of a resistor.

6. They help to stop flying leads being pulled out of a soldered joint.

7. It helps when positioning the components on the PCB and when fault-finding.

8. A2; B1; C3

9. Make sure the pad, component lead and soldering iron are at the same temperature.

Page 13

1. a) CAM
   b) CAD
   c) Machine Code
   d) C

2. Machine; CAD

3. a) Can move sideways and front to back.
   b) Can move sideways, front to back and up and down.
   c) Can move sideways, front to back, up and down and revolve.

4. accurately; 3-D

Page 14

1. a) 'Just in time' production
   b) Mass production
   c) 'One off' production
   d) Continuous production
   e) Batch production

2. a) Completely new products are rare and are more likely to be adaptations of existing designs.
   b) Because products are not intended to last forever.

3. a) Maturity
   b) Introduction
   c) Decline
   d) Growth

Page 15

1. a) i) European Standards symbol
      ii) British Standards symbol
   b) That the product meets the required standards by passing tests.
   c) Products must pass tests set by the organisations.

2. Publishes a magazine whereby similar products are tested and graded.

3. Products with in-built obsolescence soon become out of date and are disposed of.

4. a)–c) **Any three suitable answers, for example:** Mobile phone; Television; Radio: Computers; Games machines

5. recycling

Page 16

1. a) Electrolytic capacitor
   b) Diode
   c) Battery
   d) Push to break switch
   e) LDR
   f) Bell
   g) Loudspeaker
   h) Op-amp
   i) NOT Gate
   j) Microphone
   k) Motor
   l) FET

Page 17

1. a)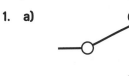

   b)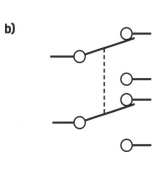

   c)

2. The number of contacts.

3. a)–b) **In any order:** Connecting two circuits together; Reversing the polarity of electric motors.

4. a) Vibration b) Proximity c) Slide d) Rocker
   e) Push f) Toggle g) Micro h) Rotary i) Key
   j) Tilt k) Reed

Page 18

1. It's a very dangerous power supply that can cause injury or death.

2. Chemical

3. a)–b) **Any two from:** Voltage; Type; Physical size; Cost

4. b) C c) AA d) AAA e) PP3

5. a) Zinc carbon
   b) Alkaline
   c) Silver oxide
   d) Lithium
   e) Nickel cadmium

Page 19

1. **a)–b) In any order:** Limit the amount of current; Set voltage levels.

2. **a)** 150R **b)** 1K8 **c)** 3R3 **d)** 12M **e)** 5K6 **f)** 10R
   g) 82M **h)** 47R **i)** 3K3 **j)** 7R5

3. **a)** 1,500 5% **b)** 220,000 10% **c)** 47 10%
   d) 56,000,000 5% **e)** 75,000 5%

Page 20

1. For maximum coverage without unnecessary overlapping of sizes.

2. **a)** 560 **b)** Blue **c)** Silver **d)** 330,000 **e)** Orange
   f) Silver **g)** 7,500 **h)** Green **i)** Gold **j)** 6,800 10%
   k) Grey **l)** 24,000 5% **m)** Red

3. **a)–b) In any order:** The tolerance 5% (gold band) and 10% (silver band); E12 has 12 resistors, E24 has 24 resistors

4.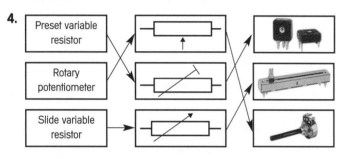

Preset variable resistor

Rotary potentiometer

Slide variable resistor

5. **a)** To protect the component connected to the resistor by limiting the amount of current flowing.

   b) i)–ii) In any order: LED; Transistor

Page 21

1. C, D and H

2. **a)** 0.5A
   b) 0.0045A, or, 4.5mA
   c) 8V
   d) 3K

Page 22

1. **a)** 900 Ohms
   b) 24K2 Ohms

2. **a) i)** 1.5V **ii)** 3V **iii)** 4.5V
   b) 9V

Page 23

1. **a)** 5 Ohms **b)** 12 Ohms

2. **a) i)** 9mA, or, 0.009A
   ii) 4.5mA, or, 0.0045A
   b) 13.5mA

Page 24

1. **a)** 3V **b)** 4V **c)** 1.5V

2. **a)** R1 = 10K, R2 = 20K
   Explanation: The ratio of the resistors, one-third and

two-thirds of the total resistance, determines the voltage output.
   b) R1 = 30K, R2 = 10K
   Explanation: The ratio of the resistors, one-quarter and three-quarters, determines the voltage output.

Page 25

1. **a)** changing **b)** variable **c)** light **d)** temperature
   e) negative

2. The switching level can be set.

3. **a)** As the light increases, the resistance of the LDR decreases and Vout becomes larger.
   b)

Page 26

1. C, D and G
2. **a)** 400 Ohms   430 Ohms
   b) 0.09 Watts or 90mW

3. 200 Ohms 220 Ohms

Page 27

1. Electrical charge

2. **a)–b) In any order:** Time delays; Smooth power supplies

3. A and D

4. **a) i)** Microfarad
   ii) 10^{-6}
   b) i) Nanofarad
   ii) 10^{-9}
   c) i) Picofarad
   ii) 10^{-12}

5. **a)** 1 second **b)** 4.7 seconds

Page 28

1. **a)** The time it takes a capacitor to charge to two-thirds of the supply voltage.
   b) Each time constant is equal to two-thirds of the remaining supply voltage.

2. The large tolerance of + or −20% results in the numbers overlapping.

3. **a) i)** +
   ii)

4. **a)–c) In any order:** Large values for electrolytic capacitors; Small values for non-electrolytic capacitors; Electrolytic capacitors are only available in three sizes. Non-electrolytic capacitors are accurate when timing.

Page 29

1. **a)**

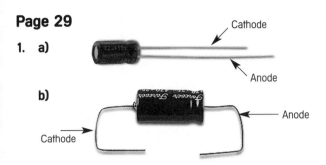

   Cathode — Anode

   b)

   Anode — Cathode

2. **a)** 5 μF **b)** 0.5 μF **c)** 11 μF **d)** 6.8 μF

Page 30

1. Capacitors in series results in a smaller value.

2. **a)** 200 μF **b)** 9.4 μF **c)** 32 μF **d)** 517 μF

Page 31

1. **a)** A component that only allows current to flow in one direction.

   b) i) Cathode   **ii)** Cathode

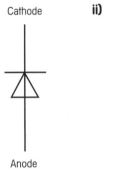

   Anode   Anode

2. **a)** Diode points towards switch. **b)** Diode points towards lamp.

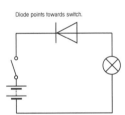   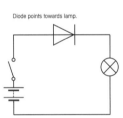

3. back emf; incorrect; polarity

Page 32

1. **a)** A special type of diode that gives out light when current passes through it.

   b) i) Anode   **ii)**

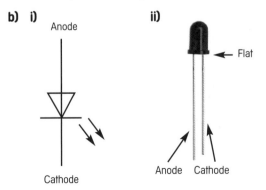

   ← Flat

   Cathode   Anode Cathode

---

2. To protect the LED by limiting the current to a safe level.

3. **a) i)** 350 ohms
      ii) 390R. Always select the nearest larger resistor.
   b) i) 500 ohms
      ii) 510R. Always select the nearest larger resistor.

Page 33

1.

2	LED3	D2	D7
3	LED4	D3	D6
4	LED5	D4	D5
5	LED6	None	None
6	LED5	D5	D4
7	LED4	D6	D3
8	LED3	D7	D2
9	LED2	D8	D1

Page 34

Number Provided	Segment Lit						
	a	b	c	d	e	f	g
0	✔	✔	✔	✔	✔	✔	
1		✔	✔				
2	✔	✔		✔	✔		✔
3	✔	✔	✔	✔			✔
4		✔	✔			✔	✔
5	✔		✔	✔		✔	✔
6	✔		✔	✔	✔	✔	✔
7	✔	✔	✔				
8	✔	✔	✔	✔	✔	✔	✔
9	✔	✔	✔	✔		✔	✔

1.

2. cathode leads

3. A variation in LED brightness will occur depending upon the number displayed.

Page 35

1. current; electronic; field

2. a)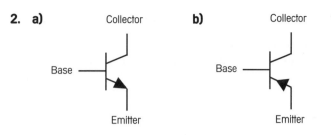

b)

3. The direction of current through the transistor, which is indicated by the arrow on the emitter.

4. a) True **b)** False **c)** False **d)** True **e)** True
 f) False **g)** True

Page 36

1. The gain of a transistor is the ratio between the base current and the collector current.

2. a) 200
 b) 40

3. 2.5mA

4. 140mA

Page 37

1. a) Protect the circuit against incorrect battery polarity.
 b) Limit the current to the transistor to a safe level.
 c) It is the current limiting resistor to protect the LED.
 d) To set the switching level.

2. a) **i)–ii) Any two suitable answers, for example:** LDR; Thermistor; Moisture Sensor; Any switch
 b) 8,800

Page 38

1. a)

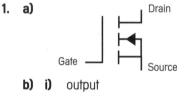

 b) i) output
 ii) input signal
 iii) OV

2. a) greater than
 b) less than

3. digital; triggered

4. Logic ICs can only respond to digital switching. Logic ICs and PICs can only source a low current.

5. a) The gate is connected to +V and goes from high resistance to low resistance, allowing current to flow from the drain into the source.
 b) To protect the transistor from back emf.

Page 39

1. a)

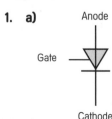

b) i) input signal
 ii) output
 iii) OV

2. bistable

3. a) When a voltage of more than 2V is applied to the gate.
 b) Once switched on, a thyristor stays on until reset.
 c) Interrupting the current flow through the thyristor by switching off the circuit, or, shorting across the anode and cathode.

4. a) Red
 b) Any colour except red or black
 c) Black

Page 40

1. a) The gate is taken above 2V.
 b) The buzzer goes off.
 c) The pulsing action of a buzzer can turn a thyristor off. The 1K resistor provides a second current path.

2. a) 100K resistor connected to OV and 1K resistor. Touch contacts connected to +V and the 1K resistor.
 b) **Any suitable answer, for example:** Copper; Brass; Any conductive material

Page 41

1. a) i) True
 ii) True
 iii) False
 b) i)–iii) **In any order:** Relays are bulky; Relays are expensive; Relays have slow switching speeds

2. A2; B9; C8; D3; E4; F5; G7; H1; I6

3. electromagnetic; electrical current; coil; plunger

Page 42

1. a) resistance
 b) 0.7
 c) on
 d) relay contacts

2. electrical; collector; emitter; transistor

Page 43

1. a) toy
 b) **In any order:** forward; reverse
 c) current; coil
 d) gearbox

2. a) **In any order:** forward; reverse
 b) microcontroller
 c) 1.8 degrees and 200 steps, or 7.5 degrees and 48 steps
 d) **In any order:** Expensive; Limited to low power use

3. a)–b) In any order: Expensive; Only suitable for low power use

4. Solder a 220nF polyester non-polarised capacitor to the contacts.

Page 44

1. **a)** 220 **b)** 40 **c)** 8,800 **d)** 100mA **e)** 1 amp
   f) 2 **g)** 7 **h)** 8

2. **a)–c) Any three from**: Smaller PCB; Fewer components; Cheaper circuit; Less soldering

3. A and B

4. Changing the input pins from high to low.

5. transistors

6. **a)–c) In any order:** Motor; Relay; Solenoid

Page 45

1. **a)** polar; electrical
   b) flying; PCB

2. **a)** **In any order:** electrical; mechanical
   b) sounds; buzzers
   c) **In any order:** input; output.

3. **a)** electrical / mechanical; mechanical / electrical
   b) electromagnetism
   c) coil; electromagnet
   d) **In any order:** attracts; repels

Page 46

1. A complete miniature electronic circuit on a silicon chip.

2. Connecting pins are arranged in two parallel lines.

3. **a)** soldering; removed
   b) It identifies the position of Pin 1.

4. **a)** **Any suitable answer, for example:** Egg timer; Courtesy timer; Games timer
   b) Flashing warning sign

5. **a)** Bottom centre, Pin 1
   b) Top right, Pin 4
   c) Top left, Pin 8
   d) Notch is between pins 1 and 8.

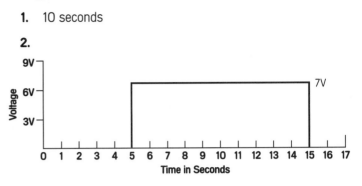

Page 47

1. A3; B7; C2; D8; E1; F5; G4; H6

2. **a)** **i)** timed state
   ii) stable state
   b) The 555 IC uses 2V internally to make it work.
   c) **i)** high
   ii) low

Page 48

1. **a)** Protects the circuit against incorrect battery polarity.
   b) To keep pin 2 at +V until triggered.
   c) **i)** High
   ii) Low
   d) Current is sinking into Pin 3.
   e) **i)** Pin 2 taken low to OV.
   ii) Pin 3 goes high.
   f) Current is sourcing out of Pin 3.
   g) They are timing components that determine the time constant.

Page 49

1. 10 seconds

2.

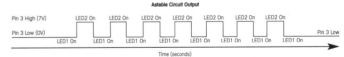

3. 1,000 seconds

Page 50

1. **a)** Pin 2 is low, the capacitor less than one-third of battery voltage.
   b) Pin 3 high, sourcing current.
   c) Capacitor charges to two-thirds of the battery voltage.
   d) Current sinking into pin 3.
   e) To protect the LEDs by limiting the amount of current to a safe level.

Page 51

1. Hertz

2. 0.68 Hertz

3. Non-electrolytic capacitors have an accuracy of ±1%.

4. The capacitor charges through R1 and R2 but only discharges through R2.

5. **a)** R1 = 1K
   b) R2 = 1M

Page 52

1. **a)** connects
   b) 2
   c) high; R1; C1
   d) high
   e) Frequency

2.

Page 53

1. A2; B3; C8; D4; E6; F7

2. **a)** 2
   b) 1

3. **a)** Two batteries in series with +V at the top, -V at the bottom and OV tapped off where the two batteries connect.

b)

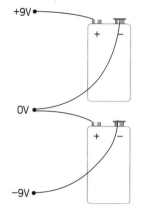

PP3 Batteries in Series

Page 54

1. **a)** False **b)** True **c)** False **d)** False **e)** True

2. **a)** High **b)** Low **c)** High **d)** Low **e)** Low

3. The output goes low to 0V.

Page 55

1. **a) i)** Potentiometer
       ii) Thermistor
    b) i) decreases
       ii) LED2
    c) LED2 goes off and LED1 comes on.

2. analogue; digital

Page 56

1. 100,000

2. distortion; output

3. Negative feedback is used to set and reduce the gain of an op-amp giving greater stability.

4. **a) i)** -2 **ii)** -2V **iii)** 75K **iv)** 0.5 **v)** 20K **vi)** −5V
       vii) 120K **viii)** -10 **ix)** -10 **x)** -20V **xi)** −3
       xii) 1.1V
    b) The -20V output is larger than the voltage supply of + or − 9V.

Page 57

1. **a) i)** Diode
       ii) LDR
       iii) 555 IC
    b) monostable
    c) i) A
       ii) B
       iii) LED1
    d) i) fall; fall
       ii) low; low; LED2

Page 58

1. **a)**

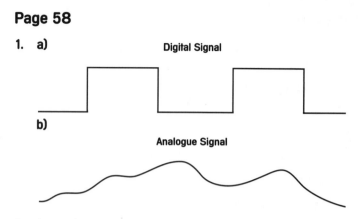

Digital Signal

b)

Analogue Signal

2. An analogue signal can confuse logic gates by constantly changing by small amounts.

3. **a)** NOT Gate

    b)
    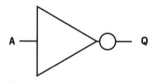

    c) Two-Input OR Gate

    d)

A	B	Q
0	0	0
0	1	1
1	0	1
1	1	1

    e)
    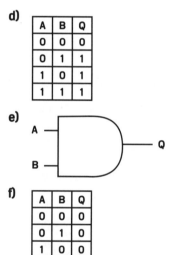

    f)

A	B	Q
0	0	0
0	1	0
1	0	0
1	1	1

4. When A and B both = 1, the output is Q for both Logic ICs and this can confuse Logic systems.

Page 59

1. **a) i)**

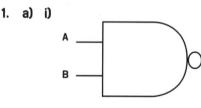

ii)

A	B	Q
0	0	1
0	1	1
1	0	1
1	1	0

    b) It is the opposite of the AND gate.

2. **a) i)**

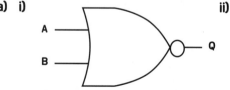

ii)

A	B	Q
0	0	1
0	1	0
1	0	0
1	1	0

    b) It is the opposite of the OR gate.

3. a) i)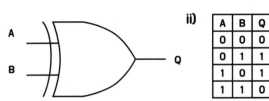

ii)

A	B	Q
0	0	0
0	1	1
1	0	1
1	1	0

b) To create the true OR gate, which would only output a 1 when A or B = 1, and overcome confusion with the AND gate.

Page 60

1. All types of logic gates can be made from NAND gates.

2. a)

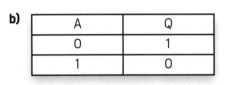

b)

A	Q
0	1
1	0

c) AND Gate

d)

A	B	C	Q
0	0	1	0
0	1	1	0
1	0	1	0
1	1	0	1

e)

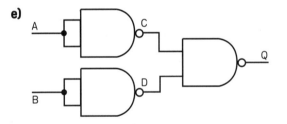

f)

A	B	C	D	Q
0	0	1	1	0
0	1	1	0	1
1	0	0	1	1
1	1	0	0	1

g)

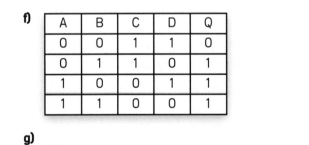

h)

A	B	C	D	E	Q
0	0	1	1	0	1
0	1	1	0	1	0
1	0	0	1	1	0
1	1	0	0	1	0

i) Exclusive OR (XOR) Gate

j)

A	B	C	D	E	Q
0	0	1	1	1	0
0	1	1	1	0	1
1	0	1	0	1	1
1	1	0	1	1	0

Page 61

1. a)

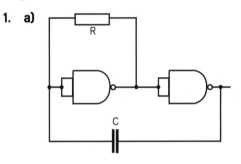

b) i) R = 1M5
ii) C = 100nF

2. a)

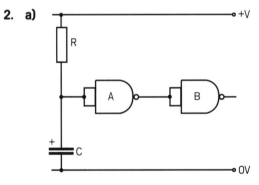

b) As the capacitor charges through the resistor, the Logic on Gate A changes from Logic 0 to Logic 1.

3. a)

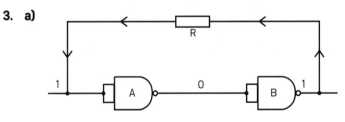

b) The 100K feedback resistor latches the signal from the output to the input. If the input changes, the output Logic is not affected due to the latch.

Page 62

1. **a)** DIL; 15V; 10; high
   b) high; generator

2. A16; B10; C9; D13; E4; F5; G14; H12; I15; J7; K1; L3; M6; N8; O11; P2

Page 63

1. Built-in seven-segment decoded output.

2. A12; B6; C4; D11; E15; F10; G13; H16; I7; J5; K14; L1; M3; N9; O2; P8

Page 64

1. **a)–b) In any order:** When the contacts of a switch are nearly touching, current can sometimes jump across the small gap and cause a rippling effect of pulses; When the contacts of a switch come together, they sometimes bounce back and forth rapidly when the switch is closed.

2. **a)**

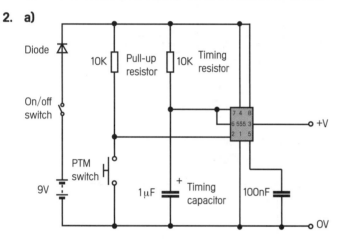

   b) When the push to make switch is pressed, pin 3 is taken high for a time constant and any switch bounce will be ignored.

3. **a)**

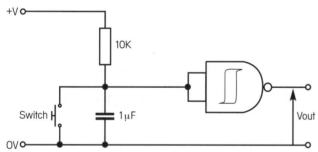

   b) When the push to make switch is pressed, switch bounce is prevented by the discharging action of the capacitor.

Page 65

1. B

2. **a)** False
   b) True

3. B

4. **a)** barrier; infra-red LED; phototransistor
   b) two

5. Phototransistors in integrated circuits

Page 66

1. A special type of IC that can be programmed to respond to input devices and control output devices.

2. B

3. **a)–c) Any three suitable examples, e.g.** Stereo equipment; DVD players; Mobile phones; Toys; Washing machines; Computer products; Alarms; Microwaves; Dishwashers.

4. **a)–b) Any two from:** PICs can replace many components; Smaller stock levels are required; Assembly time can be reduced; A programme can be altered without redesigning the PIC or changing components.

5. **a)–b) In any order:** Machine code; Assembler code

6. **a)** i)–ii) **Any two from:** Concise; Runs fast; More efficient
   b) i)–ii) **In any order:** Hard to learn; Hard to understand.

Page 67

1. **a)–b) In any order:** Basic; Flow chart

2. **a)** i)–ii) **In any order:** User friendly; Easy to learn
   b) i)–ii) **In any order:** Requires more memory; Runs slow

3. Beginners All-Purpose Symbolic Code

4. BASIC

5. B

Page 68

1. Use 3 x AA alkaline cells, or zinc carbon cells.

2. Use 4 x AA cells with a diode in series.

3. **a)**

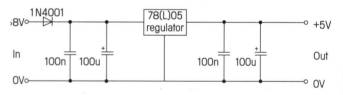

   b) The diode provides reverse connection protection.
   c) The capacitors help stabilise the 5V supply.

4. **a)–d) Any four from:** 8 pin; 14 pin; 18 pin; 20 pin; 28 pin; 40 pin

5. **a)**

   b)

   c)

d)

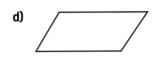

Page 69

1. The decimal system uses digits 0 to 9. The binary system uses digits 0 and 1.

2.

MSB			LSB	Decimal
0	0	0	0	0
0	0	0	1	1
0	0	1	0	2
0	0	1	1	3
0	1	0	0	4
0	1	0	1	5
0	1	1	0	6
0	1	1	1	7
1	0	0	0	8

3. **a)** Least significant bit
    b) Most significant bit

4. **a)** 13
    b) 1 1 1 0
    c) 15
    d) 0 1 1 0

Page 70

1.

	dp	g	f	e	d	c	b	a
0 =	0	0	1	1	1	1	1	1
1 =	0	0	0	0	0	1	1	0
2 =	0	1	0	1	1	0	1	1
3 =	0	1	0	0	1	1	1	1
4 =	0	1	1	0	0	1	1	0
5 =	0	1	1	0	1	1	0	1
6 =	0	1	1	1	1	1	0	1
7 =	0	0	0	0	0	1	1	1
8 =	0	1	1	1	1	1	1	1
9 =	0	1	1	0	1	1	1	1

Page 71

1. **a) i)** 1, 2 = 1
    ii) 0, 1, 3, 4, 6 = 2
    iii) 0, 1, 2, 3, 6 = 3
    iv) 1, 2, 5, 6 = 4
    v) 0, 2, 3, 5, 6 = 5
    vi) 0, 2 3, 4, 5, 6 − 6
    vii) 0, 1, 2 = 7
    viii) 0, 1, 2, 3, 4, 5, 6 = 8
    ix) 0, 1, 2, 3, 5, 6 = 9
    b) Many outputs can be controlled at the same time.
    c) i) Low or off
    ii) High or on
    d) **Any one from:** 220; 270; 330
    e) The PIC microcontroller operates so fast that, without Wait commands, the LEDs would switch on and off so quickly that the number couldn't be seen.

Page 72

1. A and E

2. Between 0 and 255.

3. low; high

4. Calibrate the analogue sensor so that a switching level can be set.

5. They inform PIC microcontrollers when to switch output devices on or off when the reading from the sensor reaches a set switching level.

6.

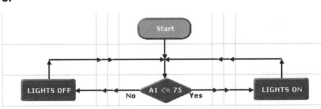

Page 73

1. True

2. Radio frequency

3. Binary signals

4. A powerful LED

5. 10; 35

6. Radio frequency

7. high; LED

Page 74

1. **Any suitable answer, for example:** 000 0000; 000 0001; 0000010

2. **a)** The length space for a 1 is wider than the space for the 0.
    b) Space coding

3. **a)–b) In any order:** Lets the TV's infra-red receiver know when to respond to a signal and when to ignore it; Reduces the chances of the receiver responding to a remote control intended for another appliance.

4. barcode; ones / zeros; zeros / ones

5. **a)–b) Any suitable answer, for example:** Barcodes on most items found in shops.

Page 75

1. **a) i)** A pull-up resistor keeping pin 1 of the infra-red receiver high.
    ii) Limits the amount of current and suppresses power supply disturbances.
    iii) Suppresses power supply disturbances.
    b) i) Output voltage
    ii) 0V
    iii) Supply voltage

2. a)–b) In any order: Photodiode; Transistor amplifier.

3. binary code, infra-red

4. True

Page 76

1. **a)** PICAXE 08M
   b) **i)** +V
      ii) Nothing
      iii) Inputs
      iv) Terminal block or infra-red receiver
      v) Piezo sounder
      vi) Transistor BC639
      vii) LED
      viii) 0V
   c) **i)** Thermistor
      ii) LDR
   d) Analogue
   e) **i)** Loudspeaker
      ii) Buzzer
      iii) Lamp
      iv) Motor

Page 77

1. **a)** **i)** Protects the circuit against the possibility of incorrect battery polarity
      ii) Protects the transistor against back emf.
      iii) Stabilises and smoothes the power supply.
      iv) A pull-down resistor.
      v) Protects the LED by limiting the amount of current.
      vi) Protects the transistor by limiting the amount of current flowing into the base.
   b) Single pole single throw
   c) 5.3V
   d) Inputs and outputs can be replaced quickly without the need for soldering.

Exam-style Questions

1.

Name	Symbol
Diode	
Fixed Resistor	
Lamp	
Push to Make Switch	
Electrolytic Capacitor	
Loudspeaker	
Variable Resistor	
LDR	

2.

Name	Symbol	Input	Process	Output	Polar Components
LED				✓	Yes
PTMS		✓			No
Transistor			✓		Yes
Buzzer				✓	Yes
Thermistor		✓			No
Thyristor			✓		Yes
NAND Gate			✓		Yes

3. **a)** LEDs
   b) LDR
   c) Op-amp
   d) Astable
   e) Op-amp
   f) An analogue signal can have any value from high to low. Digital signals only have two states, 0 and 1.
   g) **i)**

Analogue Signal

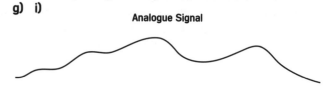

ii)

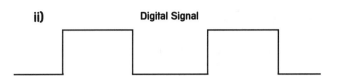

Digital Signal

h) An analogue signal can change by very small amounts.

4. a) i) Anode **ii)** Cathode
   b) Anode
   c) Cathode
   d) The flat is on the plastic case, alongside the cathode lead.

5. 350R

6. 330R

7. a)–b) In any order: 270R and 330R

8. 50R

9. a) Blue **b)** Grey **c)** Brown **d)** Gold

10. 0.18 watts

11. a) Bistable
   b) i) The gate of the thyristor receives a voltage greater than 2V and switches on.
      ii) The current flow through the thyristor is interrupted and switches off.
   c)

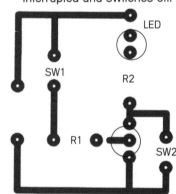

d) i)–iv) Any four from: Changes can be made quickly; Components can be positioned accurately; PCB design can be flipped through 180 degrees; The IC pin outs set at 0.1"; PCB layout can be autorouted; Can result in a small PCB.

12. A Connects battery and circuit.
   B Provides power to the circuit.
   C Provides power to drive the buzzer.
   D Protects the transistor from back emf.
   E Output device makes a sound.

13. In any order: Change – Extra transistor; **Effect –** Greater amplification and sensitivity for input.

Change – Electrolytic capacitor added; **Effect –** Creates a time delay.

14. a) i) 100K fixed resistor connected to pins 6 and 7 and +V; 22uF capacitor connected to pins 6 and 7 and 0V.
   ii) A fixed resistor connected to pin 2 and +V; A push to make switch connected to pin 2 and 0V; Resistor size 10K to 100K.

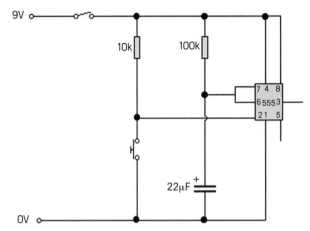

b) i) Red LED on, Green LED off
   ii) Green LED on, Red LED off. End of time constant, Green LED off and Red LED on. Red LED stays on until triggered.

15. a) Buzzer connected between pin 3 and 0V.

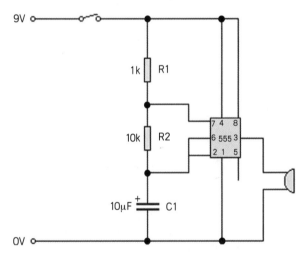

b) 0.68 Hertz
   c) Make R1 = 2K and R2 = 20K
   d) Variable resistor

16. a) R1, R2 and C1
   b) Pin 8 joined to the +9V rail.
      Pin 7 joined between R1 and R2.
      Pin 6 joined to Pin 2.
      Pins 6 and 2 are joined between R2 and C1.
      C2 joined to the loudspeaker.

b)

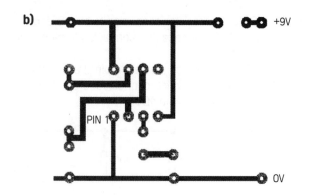

17. a) LDR
b) 3V

18. a) The light-sensing potential divider connected to Pin 3 with the LDR in the lower position.
b) A potential divider connected to pin 2, consisting of a fixed resistor and a variable resistor. The variable resistor can be in the upper or lower position.
c) Fixed resistor connected to pin 6 in series with an LED connected to 0V. The LED is pointing downwards towards 0V.

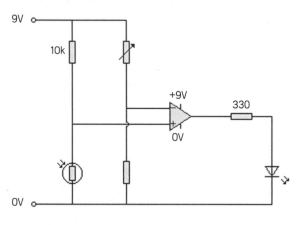

19. a) i) Single pole double throw
ii) To connect the two circuits together and provide extra power for the fan.
b) i) A potential divider consisting of two 10K fixed resistors connected to PIN 2. A potential divider with the thermistor in the upper position and a variable resistor in the lower position connected to PIN 3.

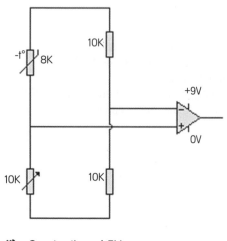

ii) Greater than 4.5V
c) 5V

20.

A	B	Q
0	0	0
0	1	1
1	0	1
1	1	1

21. 1

22. a) Input A connected to input of a gate. Input B connected to the other input of the same gate. Output of the first gate connected to the input of the second gate. Inputs of the second gate connected together. Output of the second gate connected to Q.
b) Pin 14 connected to +V. Pin 7 connected to 0V.
c) Inputs of the two unused gates connected to 0V.

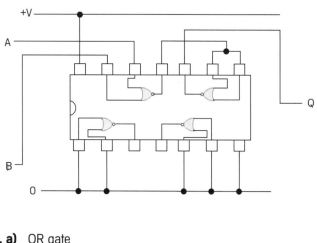

23. a) OR gate
b) NOT gate
c) AND gate
d)

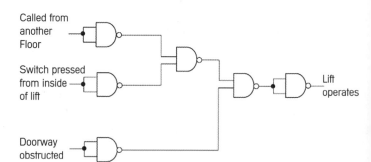

24. a) LDR; Thermistor; SPST Switch
b)

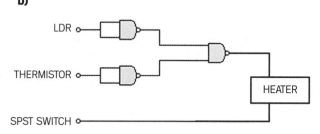

c) i)–ii) Any four from: Less ICs; Smaller PCBs; Reduced costs; Less stock; Less soldering

25. Let LED 1 = Output 1 (1)
Let LED 2 = Output 2 (2)
Let LED 3 = Output 3 (4)
Let Wand and Track = Input 0

10	if input 0 = 1 goto 20	Decision
	if input 0 = 0 goto 10	Loop
20	let pins = 1	Output LED 1 On
30	pause 2000	Wait 2 seconds
40	if input 0 = 1 goto 50	Decision
	if input 0 = 0 goto 40	Loop
50	let pins = 3	Output LEDs 1 and 2 On
60	pause 2000	Wait 2 seconds
70	if input 0 = 1 goto 80	Decision
	if input 0 = 0 goto 70	Loop
80	let pins = 7	LEDs 1, 2, 3 On
90	pause 2000	Wait 2 seconds
100	let pins = 0	LEDs 1, 2 and 3 Off
110	pause 250	Wait 0.25 seconds
120	let pins = 7	LEDs 1, 2 and 3 On
130	pause 250	Wait 0.25 seconds
140	let pins = 0	LEDs 1, 2 and 3 Off
150	pause 250	Wait 0.25 seconds
160	let pins = 7	LEDs 1, 2 and 3 On
170	pause	Wait 0.25 seconds
180	let pins = 0	LEDs 1, 2 and 3 Off
190	pause	Wait 0.25 seconds
200	let pins = 7	LEDs 1, 2 and 3 On
210	pause	Wait 0.25 seconds
220	let pins = 0	LEDs 1, 2 and 3 Off
230	goto 10	Loop

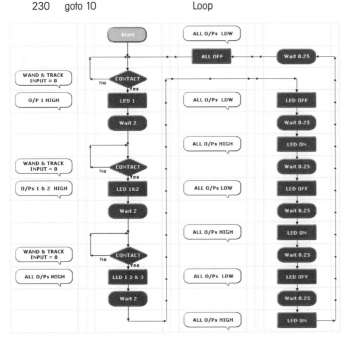

26. A Road Safety Product using BASIC

10	if input 0 = 1 goto 20	Decision Command
20	if input1 = <=75 goto 30	Compare Command
30	gosub flash leds 1 to 10	Do Procedure 10 times
40	gosub blink leds 1 to 5	Do Procedure 5 times
50	goto 10	

procedure flash leds

let output 2 = 1	LEDs A On
pause 250	Wait 0.25 secs

let output 3 = 1	LEDs B On
pause 250	Wait 0.25 secs
let output 4 = 1	LEDs C On
pause 250	Wait 0.25 secs
let output 3 = 1	LEDs B On
pause 250	Wait 0.25 secs
return	End

procedure blink leds

let outputs 2, 3 & 4 = 1	All LEDs On
pause 500	Wait 0.5 secs
let outputs = 0	All LEDs Off
pause 500	Wait 0.5 secs
return	End

A Road Safety Product using Flowchart

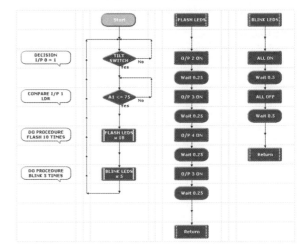

27. a) Improved graphics due to higher performance gaming consoles, or, graphics cards in PCs.

   b) i) There's a worry that players of electronic games aren't as fit as people who play active sport, leading to obesity.

      ii) Players of electronic games can become isolated from their family, spending their leisure time in their bedrooms.

   c) Manufacturers sell more games consoles by introducing a new machine every four or five years, making old consoles obsolete because they can't play the new games.

   d) European standards state that batteries and cells shouldn't be disposed of in landfill. These products can contaminate the soil for generations.

28. a) Never turn the light box on when the lid is raised.

   b) Wear plastic gloves and eye protection.

   c) Wear plastic gloves, apron, eye protection and work in a well-ventilated room.

   d) Remove rings, jewellery, roll up sleeves, tie hair back and wear eye protection.

   e) Remove rings, jewellery, roll up sleeves, tie hair back and wear eye protection, keep fingers away from the disc and work on the right hand side of the machine.

   f) Keep fingers away from hot parts of the soldering iron. Work in a well-ventilated room and wear eye protection.

29. a)–b) In any order: Mains electricity can kill; Can cause burns; Can disrupt the rhythm of the heart.

ACKNOWLEDGEMENTS

The author and publisher are grateful to the copyright holders for permission to use quoted materials and images.

With special thanks to Barbara McHugh and Jon-David McHugh for all their help and assistance.

The author and publisher are grateful to the copyright holders for permission to use quoted materials and images.

Photographs are reproduced with the kind permission of Rapid Electronics Ltd., Severalls Lane, Colchester, Essex CO4 5JS. www.rapidonline.com

With thanks to Revolution Ltd., Unit 2, Industrial Quarter, Foxcoat Avenue, Bath Business Park, Bath, BA2 8SF.

Every effort has been made to trace copyright holders and obtain their permission for the use of copyright material. The authors and publishers will gladly receive information enabling them to rectify any error or omission in subsequent editions. All facts are correct at time of going to press.

Published by Collins
An imprint of HarperCollins*Publishers*
77–85 Fulham Palace Road
London W6 8JB

© HarperCollins*Publishers* 2009

First published 2009

British Library Cataloguing in Publication Data.

A CIP record of this book is available from the British Library.

Book concept and development: Helen Jacobs
Commissioning Editor: Rebecca Skinner
Author: David McHugh
Project Editor: Robert Dean
Cover Design: Angela English
Inside Concept Design: Helen Jacobs and Sarah Duxbury
Text Design and Layout: FiSH Books
Artwork: Lonsdale

555 IC Monostable Calculations

1 Calculate the time period of the 555 IC when R = 100K and C = 100μf. Show your working.

Formula: ....

Working: ....

....

Answer with units: ....

2 Using your answer from question 1, draw a mark–space ratio diagram to show the output at pin 3 if the trigger switch was pressed at 5 seconds.

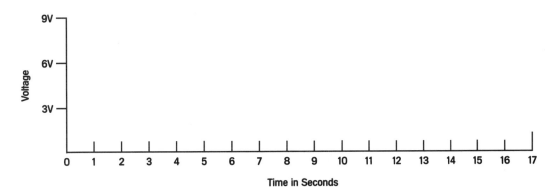

3 When a monostable circuit is designed, the maximum value of R1 should be 1M and the maximum value of C1 should be 1000μF. What time period would this monostable circuit have? Show your working.

Formula: ....

Working: ....

....

....

Answer with units: ....

1 The circuit below shows a 555 IC being used as an astable.

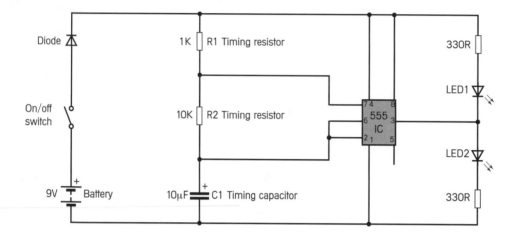

a) Why is the output voltage at pin 3 high when the circuit is first switched on?

_____

_____

b) Explain why LED2 lights up when the circuit is first switched on.

_____

c) Explain why the output voltage at pin 3 changes from high to low after the circuit is first switched on.

_____

_____

d) Explain why LED1 lights up when the output voltage at pin 3 is low.

_____

e) What is the purpose of the 330 Ohm resistors in series with the LEDs?

_____

_____

_____

1 The number of pulses a 555 IC operating in the astable mode makes in one second is called the frequency. What is the unit of measurement for frequency?

....

2 Calculate the frequency of a 555 IC Astable when R1 = 1K, R2 = 10K and C1 = 100μF

Formula: ....

Working: ....

....

....

Answer with units: ....

3 When designing an astable circuit, why should your choice for C1 be a non-electrolytic capacitor rather than an electrolytic capacitor?

....

....

....

Mark–Space Ratio

4 Why is it difficult to have an astable circuit where the output at pin 3 has an equal mark–space (on–off) ratio?

....

....

5 Suggest resistor values for R1 and R2 which will give an approximately equal mark–space (on–off) ratio.

a) R1 ....   **b)** R2 ....

Interfacing 555 ICs

1 The circuit below shows a 555 IC monostable controlling a 555 IC astable.

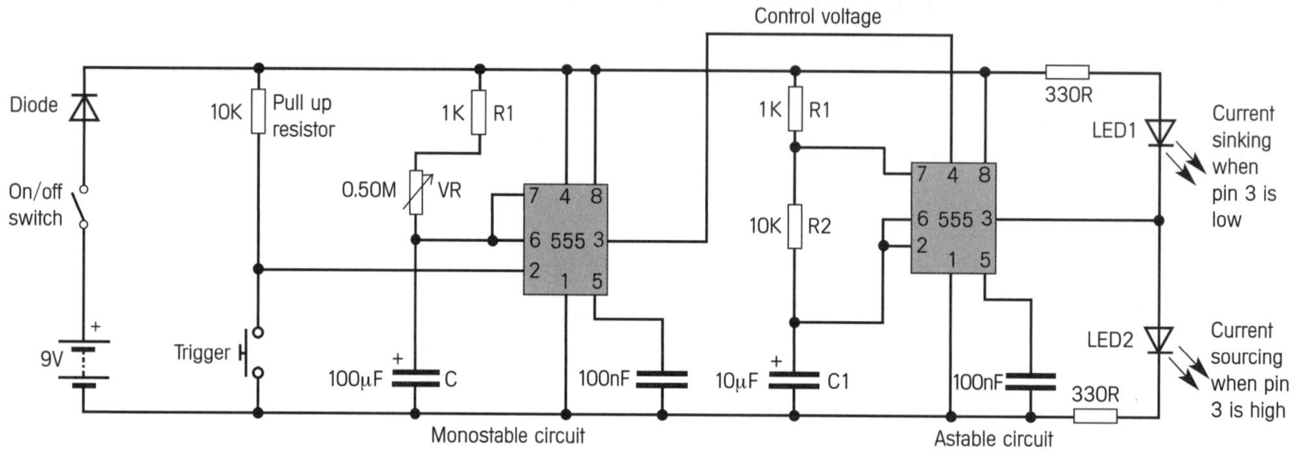

Explain how the circuit works. Fill in the missing words to complete the following sentences.

a) On/off switch _____ battery to circuit.

b) Trigger switch takes pin _____ low.

c) Pin 3 goes _____ for a time constant set by _____

and _____ .

d) Pin 4 on the astable goes _____ .

e) LEDs 1 and 2 start to flash alternately at a _____ set by R1, R2 and C1.

Mark–Space Diagrams

2 Draw a fully labelled equal mark–space ratio diagram to show what happens in the astable circuit when the output from the monostable circuit is high.

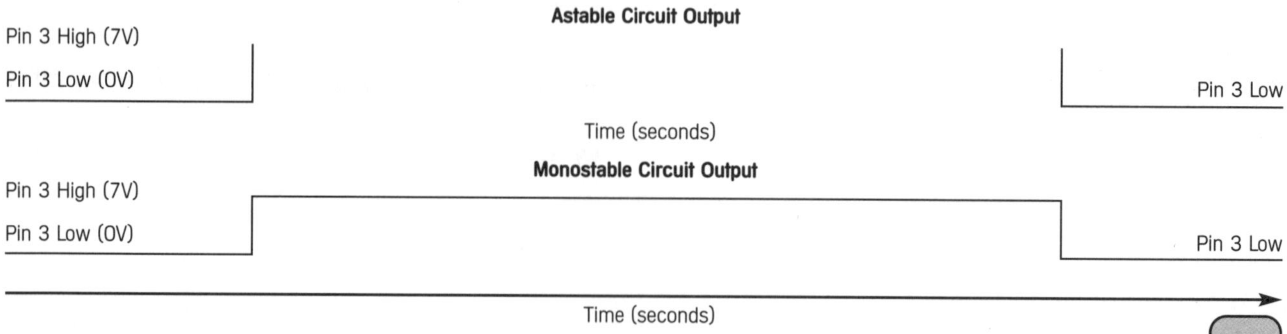

Astable Circuit Output

Monostable Circuit Output

Operational Amplifiers

Operational Amplifiers

1 The pin diagram shows an op-amp. Match **A–F** with the labels **1–7** on the diagram. Enter the appropriate number in the boxes provided. Pins 1 and 5 have been done for you.

Top View of IC Showing Identification Notch and Dot

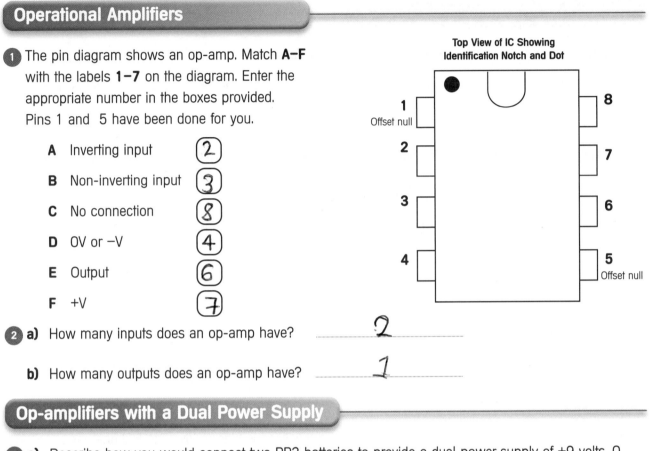

A Inverting input   (2)

B Non-inverting input   (3)

C No connection   (8)

D 0V or −V   (4)

E Output   (6)

F +V   (7)

2 a) How many inputs does an op-amp have?   *2*

b) How many outputs does an op-amp have?   *1*

Op-amplifiers with a Dual Power Supply

3 a) Describe how you would connect two PP3 batteries to provide a dual power supply of +9 volts, 0 volts and -9 volts.

Connecting two PP3 batteries in series, common connection will be . OV .

b) Draw a diagram to show how you would connect two PP3 batteries to provide a dual power supply of +9 volts, 0 volts and -9 volts.

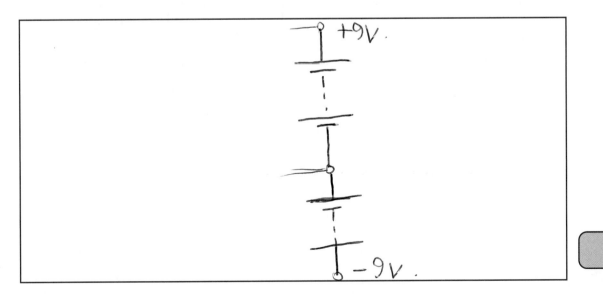

Operational Amplifiers

Operational Amplifiers

1 Are the following statements about the op-amp **true** or **false**?

a) The output of an op-amp is high voltage if the inverting input voltage is bigger than the non-inverting input voltage. ___*false*___

b) The output of an op-amp is low voltage if the non-inverting input voltage is smaller than the inverting input voltage. ___*false* *true*___

c) An op-amp can only detect large changes in voltage between the inverting and non-inverting inputs.
___*false*___

d) The output of an op-amp is low voltage if the inverting input voltage is smaller than the non-inverting input voltage. ___*false*___

e) The output of an op-amp is high voltage if the non-inverting input voltage is bigger than the inverting input voltage. ___*true*___

2 Complete the following table to say whether the output voltage is high or low. The first one has been done for you.

Pin 2	Pin 3	Pin 6	
Inverting Input Voltage	**Non-inverting Input Voltage**	**Output Voltage**	
4V	3V	Low	
3V	4V	**a)** *High*	
3.3V	2.2V	**b)** *Low*	
3.03V	3.3V	**c)** *High*	
4.10V	4.01V	**d)** *Low*	
6.01V	5.99V	**e)** *Low*	

3 Give an advantage of using a 3140 FET op-amp rather than a 741 op-amp.

___*It can switch off components that need lower voltages in order to switch off.*___

Op-amps Working as a Comparator

1 The circuit below shows an op-amp being used as a comparator.

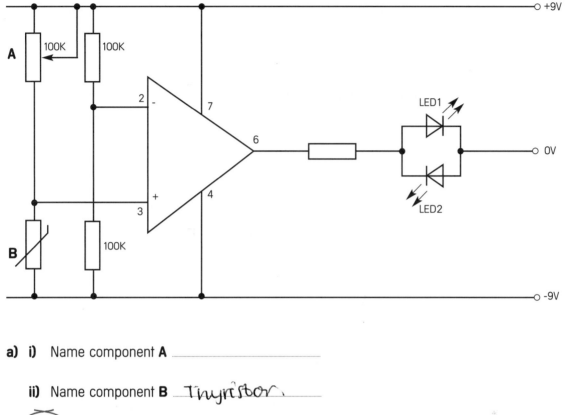

a) i) Name component **A** ....

   ii) Name component **B** *Thyristor* ....

b) ⟨Circle⟩ the correct options in the following sentences.

   i) The voltage on Pin 3 **increases / decreases** as the temperature around component B gets warmer.

   ii) The voltage input to Pin 2 is slightly greater than the voltage input to Pin 3 so **LED1 / LED2** will be lit.

c) What happens to LED1 and LED2 when the temperature gets colder?

....

2 Choose the correct words from the options given to complete the sentence below.

digital   **binary**   **analogue**   **logic**

An op-amp is an ___*analogue*___ to ___*digital*___ . convertor.

Op-amp as an Inverting Amplifier

The Operational Amplifier Working as an Inverting Amplifier AQA

1. What is the approximate gain of an op-amp in open loop?

....

2. Fill in the missing words to complete the following sentence.

Open loop gain is sometimes unwanted because it can cause .... by

clipping the .... signal.

3. What is negative feedback used for? ....

....

4. The diagram shows an op-amp being used as an inverting amplifier.

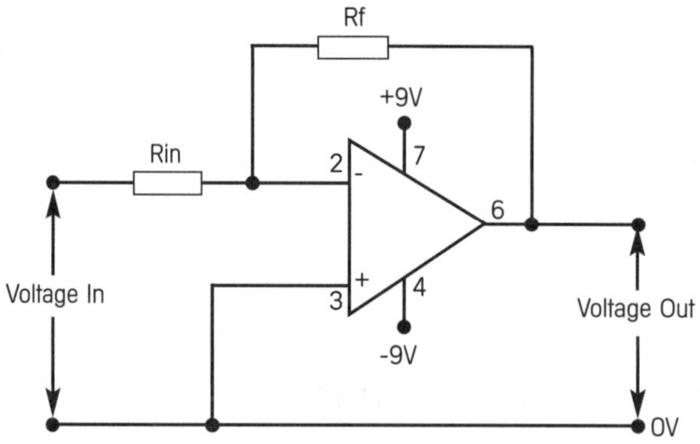

a) Complete the following table.

R_f	R_{in}	Gain	Voltage in	Voltage out
20K	10K	**i)**	1 volt	**ii)** ....
iii)	15K	–5	**iv)**	–2.5 volts
20K	**v)**	–1	5 volts	**vi)** ....
vii)	12K	**viii)**	0.5 volts	–5 volts
470K	47K	**ix)**	2 volts	**x)** ....
390K	130K	**xi)**	**xii)**	–3.3 volts

b) Which of the above would result in clipping? Explain your choice.

....

....

Interfacing a 555 IC and an Op-Amp

1 The diagram below shows an op-amp operating as a voltage comparator.

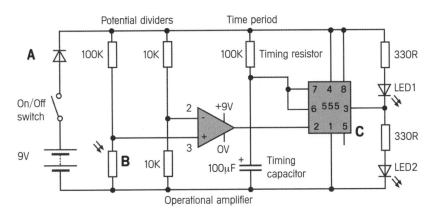

a) Name components **A**, **B** and **C** in the diagram.

i) A ....

ii) B ....

iii) C ....

b) (Circle) the correct option in the following sentence.

Component C is being used as a(n) **monostable / astable**.

c) In darkness the resistance of component B is about 1OM and in bright light its resistance is about 1K.

i) What is the output voltage of the op-amp potential divider in darkness? Tick the correct option.

A High voltage ◯

B Low voltage ◯

ii) What would be the voltage at pin 3 of component C? Tick the correct option.

A High voltage ◯

B Low voltage ◯

iii) Would LED1 or LED2 be lit? ....

d) (Circle) the correct options in the following sentences.

i) In bright light, the resistance of the LDR will **rise / fall**. The voltage on pin 3 of the op-amp will **rise / fall** below the voltage on pin 2 of the op-amp.

ii) Pin 6 will change to **high / low** voltage, taking pin 2 of the 555 IC **high / low**. Pin 3 goes high and **LED1 / LED2** is lit.

Logic Gates and Truth Tables

1 Sketch a digital signal and an analogue signal in the boxes below.

a) Digital

b) Analogue

2 Logic gates are digital electronic devices. Why can't they cope with analogue signals?

....

....

3 Complete the following table.

Name of Gate	Symbol	Truth Table
a)	**b)**	<table><tr><td>A</td><td>Q</td></tr><tr><td>1</td><td>0</td></tr><tr><td>0</td><td>1</td></tr></table>
c)	A ———⟩ Q B ———⟩	**d)** <table><tr><td>A</td><td>B</td><td>Q</td></tr><tr><td>0</td><td>0</td><td></td></tr><tr><td>0</td><td>1</td><td></td></tr><tr><td>1</td><td>0</td><td></td></tr><tr><td>1</td><td>1</td><td></td></tr></table>
Two-input AND	**e)**	**f)** <table><tr><td>A</td><td>B</td><td>Q</td></tr><tr><td>0</td><td>0</td><td></td></tr><tr><td>0</td><td>1</td><td></td></tr><tr><td>1</td><td>0</td><td></td></tr><tr><td>1</td><td>1</td><td></td></tr></table>

4 What similarities are there between the two-input AND gate and the two-input OR gate?

....

....

Symbols and Truth Tables

1 a) Draw the symbol and complete the truth table for a two-input NAND gate.

Logic Symbol	Truth Table		
i)	ii)		
	A	B	Q
	0	0	
	0	1	
	1	0	
	1	1	

b) A NAND gate means NOT AND. What does this mean?

2 a) Draw and label the symbol and complete the truth table for a two-input NOR gate.

Logic Symbol	Truth Table		
i)	ii)		
	A	B	Q
	0	0	
	0	1	
	1	0	
	1	1	

b) A NOR gate means NOT OR. What does this mean?

3 a) Draw and label the symbol and complete the truth table for a two-input EXCLUSIVE OR (XOR) gate.

Logic Symbol	Truth Table		
i)	ii)		
	A	B	Q
	0	0	
	0	1	
	1	0	
	1	1	

b) Why was the EXCLUSIVE OR gate developed from the OR gate?

Universal Building Block

Universal Building Block   Edexcel • OCR

1 Why is the NAND logic gate often referred to as the universal building block?

....

....

2 Complete the following table by either naming the gate, drawing the symbol or filling in the truth table.

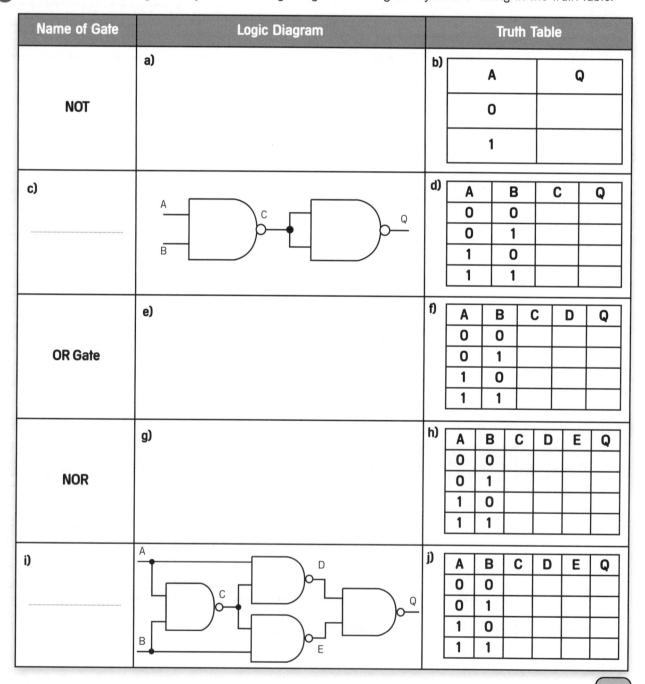

Name of Gate	Logic Diagram	Truth Table
NOT	a)	b) <table><tr><td>A</td><td>Q</td></tr><tr><td>0</td><td></td></tr><tr><td>1</td><td></td></tr></table>
c)	(NAND diagram with inputs A, B, output C, then to Q)	d) <table><tr><td>A</td><td>B</td><td>C</td><td>Q</td></tr><tr><td>0</td><td>0</td><td></td><td></td></tr><tr><td>0</td><td>1</td><td></td><td></td></tr><tr><td>1</td><td>0</td><td></td><td></td></tr><tr><td>1</td><td>1</td><td></td><td></td></tr></table>
OR Gate	e)	f) <table><tr><td>A</td><td>B</td><td>C</td><td>D</td><td>Q</td></tr><tr><td>0</td><td>0</td><td></td><td></td><td></td></tr><tr><td>0</td><td>1</td><td></td><td></td><td></td></tr><tr><td>1</td><td>0</td><td></td><td></td><td></td></tr><tr><td>1</td><td>1</td><td></td><td></td><td></td></tr></table>
NOR	g)	h) <table><tr><td>A</td><td>B</td><td>C</td><td>D</td><td>E</td><td>Q</td></tr><tr><td>0</td><td>0</td><td></td><td></td><td></td><td></td></tr><tr><td>0</td><td>1</td><td></td><td></td><td></td><td></td></tr><tr><td>1</td><td>0</td><td></td><td></td><td></td><td></td></tr><tr><td>1</td><td>1</td><td></td><td></td><td></td><td></td></tr></table>
i)	(NAND logic diagram with inputs A, B, internal C, D, E, output Q)	j) <table><tr><td>A</td><td>B</td><td>C</td><td>D</td><td>E</td><td>Q</td></tr><tr><td>0</td><td>0</td><td></td><td></td><td></td><td></td></tr><tr><td>0</td><td>1</td><td></td><td></td><td></td><td></td></tr><tr><td>1</td><td>0</td><td></td><td></td><td></td><td></td></tr><tr><td>1</td><td>1</td><td></td><td></td><td></td><td></td></tr></table>

Circuits Made from NAND Gates

Astable Circuits

1 a) Draw an astable circuit made from two NAND gates, a fixed resistor and a non-electrolytic capacitor.

b) Suggest component values for the resistor and the capacitor.

    i) Resistor _____

    ii) Capacitor _____

Time Delay Circuits

2 a) Draw a time delay circuit made from two NAND gates, a fixed resistor and an electrolytic capacitor.

b) Explain how the circuit works. _____

_____

Latch Circuits

3 a) Draw an electronic latch circuit made from two NAND gates and a fixed resistor.

b) Explain how the circuit works and the direction of feedback.

_____

_____

4017 IC Decade Counter

1 Fill in the missing words to complete the following sentences.

a) The 4017 IC decade counter is available in a 16 pin _____ package and can

operate between 3V and _____. The IC consists of _____

outputs, which can be reset back to the first output if fewer than 10 outputs are needed. Only one

output is _____ at any one time.

b) If LEDs are connected to the output pins, they will each go _____ in their set

order. The speed at which the LED turns on and off will depend on the speed of the pulse

_____ or clock, which is connected to the decade counter.

2 The pin diagram of a 4017 IC is shown below. Match **A–P** with the labels **1–16** on the diagram. Enter
the appropriate number in the boxes provided.

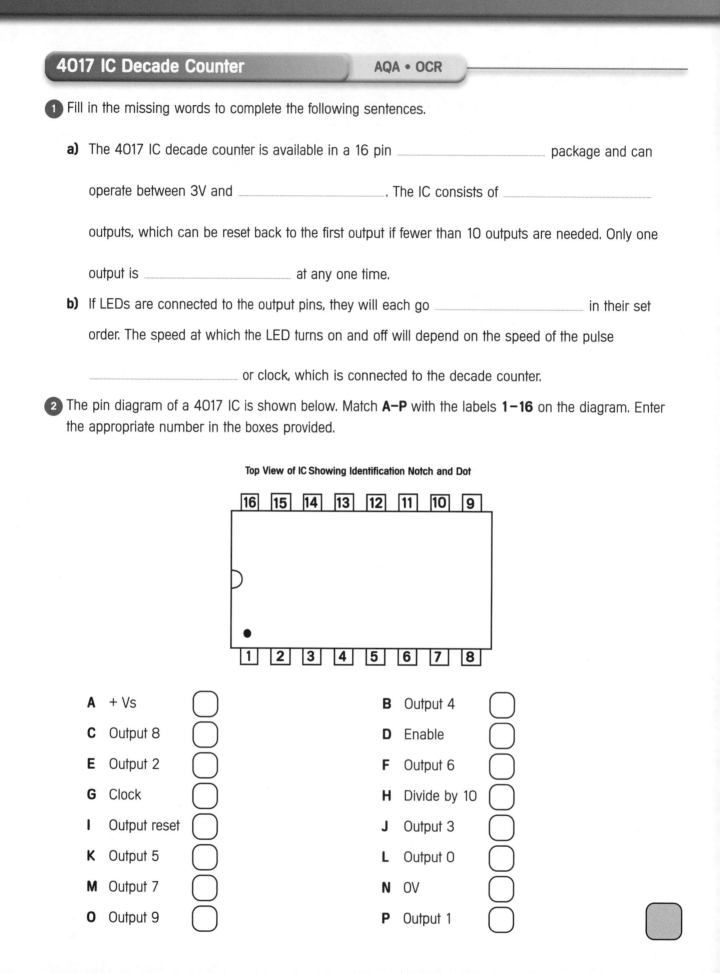

Top View of IC Showing Identification Notch and Dot

A	+ Vs	◯		B	Output 4	◯
C	Output 8	◯		D	Enable	◯
E	Output 2	◯		F	Output 6	◯
G	Clock	◯		H	Divide by 10	◯
I	Output reset	◯		J	Output 3	◯
K	Output 5	◯		L	Output 0	◯
M	Output 7	◯		N	0V	◯
O	Output 9	◯		P	Output 1	◯

4026 IC Decade Counter

AQA • OCR

1 Complete the following sentence.

The 4026 IC is a decade counter with a _____

_____

2 The pin diagram of a 4026 IC is shown below. Match **A–P** with the labels **1–16** on the diagram. Enter the appropriate number in the boxes provided.

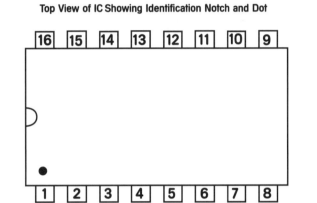

Top View of IC Showing Identification Notch and Dot

A	Segment B	◯	**B**	Segment F	◯
C	Display enable (Out) (use for decimal point)	◯	**D**	Segment E	◯
E	Reset connected to 0V	◯	**F**	Segment A	◯
G	Segment C	◯	**H**	Power supply connected to +V	◯
I	Segment G	◯	**J**	Carry out – (to another 4026)	◯
K	Ungated 'C' segment leave unconnected	◯	**L**	Clock input	◯
M	Display enable (In) connected to +V	◯	**N**	Segment D	◯
O	Clock inhibit connected to 0V	◯	**P**	Ground pin connected to 0V	◯

Switch Bounce

1 Describe two ways in which 'switch bounce' occurs when using mechanical switches.

a) ....

b) ....

Eliminating Switch Bounce   AQA

2 a) Draw a diagram to illustrate a way of overcoming switch bounce in electronic circuits using a monostable circuit.

b) Explain how the circuit you have drawn works.

....

....

....

Schmitt Trigger Switch De-bouncing Circuit   AQA

3 a) Draw a diagram to illustrate a way of overcoming switch bounce in electronic circuits using a Schmitt trigger.

b) Explain how the circuit you have drawn works.

....

....

....

1 What can electrical noise created by cheap d.c. motors do to a PIC microcontroller? Tick the correct option.

    A Nothing ◯

    B Cause damage ◯

    C Make it run better ◯

    D Make it last longer ◯

2 Is the following statement **true** or **false**?

    a) Using an optoisolator does **not** protect a PIC microcontroller from the electrical noise created by a motor. ....

    b) Optoisolators can be used to overcome electrical noise. ....

3 What can be found inside an optoisolator? Tick the correct option.

    A Infra-red light emitting diode and a capacitor ◯

    B Infra-red light emitting diode and a phototransistor ◯

    C Infra-red light emitting diode and a transistor ◯

    D Infra-red light emitting diode and a 555 IC ◯

4 Choose the correct words from the options given to complete the sentences below.

SIL   DIL   capacitor   voltage

infra-red LED   one   barrier   transistor

phototransistor   optoisolator   two   circuits

    a) The PIC microcontroller is isolated from the motor it is controlling by the ....

    between the .... and the ....

    b) The TLP504A contains .... optoisolators in a discrete 8 pin IC.

5 What have replaced phototransistors in switching circuits?

....

PIC Microcontrollers

Introduction to PICs

1 What is a PIC microcontroller?

(Integrated circuit)

It is a computer chip ib's an IC that can be programmed to respond to input devices a also controu output devices.

2 Why are PICs often referred to as a computer in a chip? Tick the correct option.

A PICs have the same power as a computer ☐

B Inside a PIC are all the parts of a computer ☑

C PICs can be used as personal computers ☐

3 PIC microcontrollers are used in all types of consumer goods. List three products that might include a PIC as part of their electronic circuitry.

a) stereo equipment

b) DVD players

c) alarms.

4 Give two advantages of using a PIC microcontroller.

a) Pic replaces many components

b) they can alter programme withhoub re-designing the PCB.

Low Level Programming

5 Name two low level programming languages.

a)

b)

6 a) What are the advantages of low level programming language?

i)

ii)

b) What are the disadvantages of low level programming language?

i)

ii)

PICs and Power Supplies

High Level Programming

1 Name two high level programming languages.

a) ....

b) ....

2 What are the advantages of high level programming language?

a) i) ....

ii) ....

b) What are the disadvantages of high level programming language?

i) ....

ii) ....

3 What do the letters BASIC stand for?

....

4 Is it better to use flow chart or BASIC for complicated and large programmes?

....

Batteries

5 At what voltages do PIC microcontrollers run programmes? Tick the correct option.

A Between 1 and 3.V d.c. ◯

B Between 3 and 5.5V d.c. ◯

C Between 5 and 10V d.c. ◯

D Between 7 and 8.5V d.c. ◯

PIC and PICAXE Microcontrollers

Batteries and Regulated Low Voltage Power Supply

1 Explain how you would make a supply voltage range of 4.5V.

$1.5 \times 3 = 4.5v$ 3xAA alkaline cell

2 Explain how you would make a supply voltage of 5.3V.

$6V - 0.7 = 5.3v$ 4xAA alkaline cells in Series with diode

3 a) Draw a 9V d.c. supply regulated to 5V using a voltage regulator.

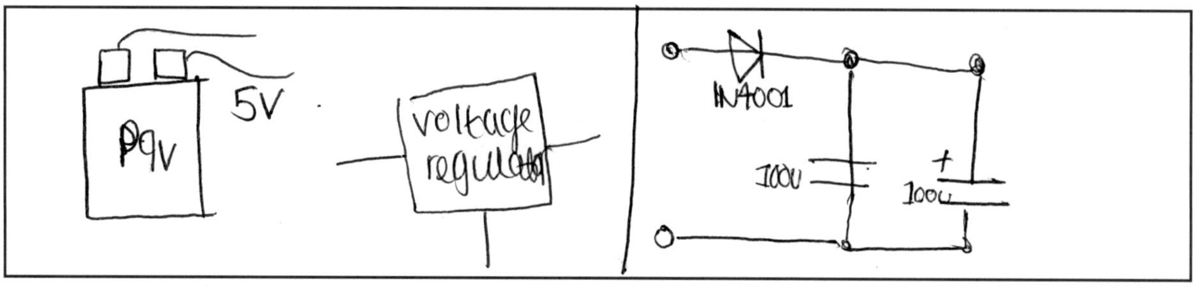

b) What does the diode do in the circuit?

Reduce the voltage ; reverse connection protection

c) What do the capacitors do in the circuit?

Stabilise the 5v supply.

PICAXE Microcontrollers

4 List four sizes of PICAXE microcontrollers.

a) _____   **b)** _____

c) _____   **d)** _____

Flow Chart Symbols

5 Draw the following flow chart symbols.

a) Terminator	**b)** Decision	**c)** Process	**d)** Input / Output

Binary and Decimal Systems

1 What's the difference between the decimal system of counting and the binary system of counting?

....

....

2 Complete the binary table below. The first and last lines have been done for you.

MSB			LSB	DECIMAL
0	0	0	0	0
				1
				2
				3
				4
				5
				6
				7
1	0	0	0	8

3 a) What does 'LSB' stand for? ....

b) What does 'MSB' stand for? ....

Converting Binary and Decimal

4 a) Convert the binary number 1101 to decimal. ....

....

b) Convert the decimal number 14 to binary. ....

....

c) Convert the binary number 1111 to decimal. ....

....

d) Convert the decimal number 6 to binary. ....

....

Using Binary Numbers

Programming in Binary

1 The diagram below shows a PIC microcontroller and the connections to a seven-segment display.

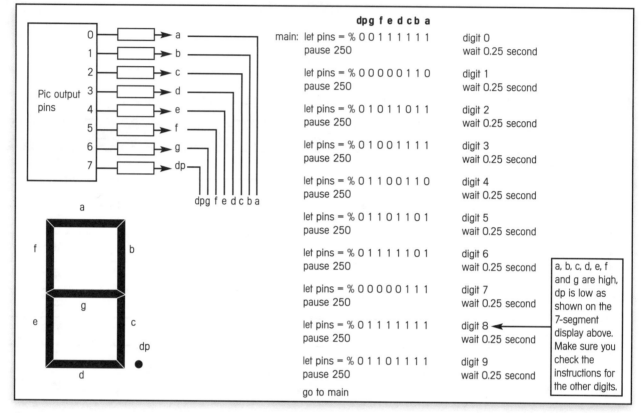

```
                                          dpg f e d c b a
                              main:  let pins = % 0 0 1 1 1 1 1 1      digit 0
                                     pause 250                        wait 0.25 second

                                     let pins = % 0 0 0 0 0 1 1 0      digit 1
                                     pause 250                        wait 0.25 second

                                     let pins = % 0 1 0 1 1 0 1 1      digit 2
                                     pause 250                        wait 0.25 second

                                     let pins = % 0 1 0 0 1 1 1 1      digit 3
                                     pause 250                        wait 0.25 second

                                     let pins = % 0 1 1 0 0 1 1 0      digit 4
                                     pause 250                        wait 0.25 second

                                     let pins = % 0 1 1 0 1 1 0 1      digit 5
                                     pause 250                        wait 0.25 second

                                     let pins = % 0 1 1 1 1 1 0 1      digit 6
                                     pause 250                        wait 0.25 second

                                     let pins = % 0 0 0 0 0 1 1 1      digit 7
                                     pause 250                        wait 0.25 second

                                     let pins = % 0 1 1 1 1 1 1 1      digit 8  ←
                                     pause 250                        wait 0.25 second

                                     let pins = % 0 1 1 0 1 1 1 1      digit 9
                                     pause 250                        wait 0.25 second

                              go to main
```

a, b, c, d, e, f and g are high, dp is low as shown on the 7-segment display above. Make sure you check the instructions for the other digits.

Complete the table to show which binary numbers are needed to make the seven-segment display show the numbers 0 to 9. The number 0 has been done for you.

Segment Letters

	dp	g	f	e	d	c	b	a
0 =	0	0	1	1	1	1	1	1
1 =								
2 =								
3 =								
4 =								
5 =								
6 =								
7 =								
8 =								
9 =								

Programming by Flow Chart

Logicator for PIC Micros

1 The diagram shows a PIC microcontroller and the connections to a seven-segment display.

a) Complete the following flow chart by entering the PIC microcontroller pin numbers alongside the output command boxes to make the seven-segment display show the numbers 0 to 9. Number 0 has been done for you.

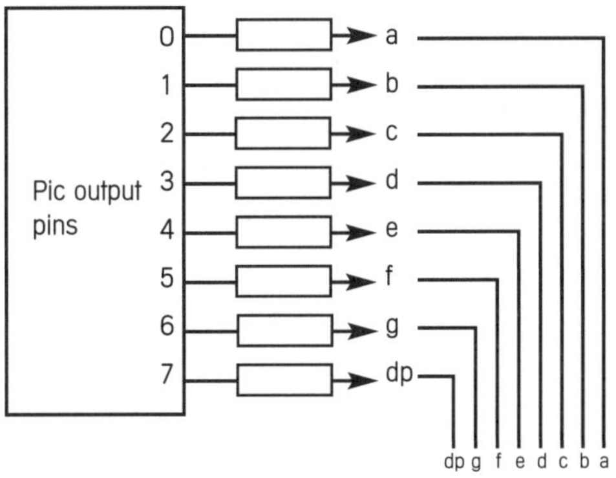

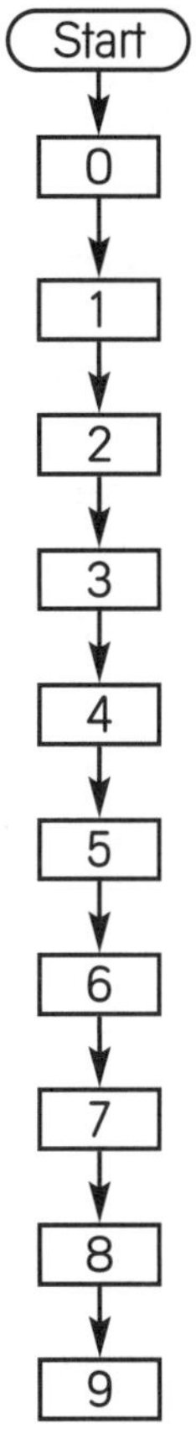

Start

| 0 | O = Output Pins 0, 1, 2, 3, 4, 5

| 1 | **i)** 1 = Output Pins _____

| 2 | **ii)** 2 = Output Pins _____

| 3 | **iii)** 3 = Output Pins _____

| 4 | **iv)** 4 = Output Pins _____

| 5 | **v)** 5 = Output Pins _____

| 6 | **vi)** 6 = Output Pins _____

| 7 | **vii)** 7 = Output Pins _____

| 8 | **viii)** 8 = Output Pins _____

| 9 | **ix)** 9 = Output Pins _____

Pic output pins: 0 → a, 1 → b, 2 → c, 3 → d, 4 → e, 5 → f, 6 → g, 7 → dp

dp g f e d c b a

b) Give an advantage of using binary numbers when working with PIC microcontrollers.

....

c) i) What does the number 0 indicate when programming?

....

ii) What does the number 1 indicate when programming?

....

d) Give the size of a suitable resistor that could be used to protect the seven-segment display.

....

e) What would be the purpose of placing a Wait command between each of the output commands?

....

....

Analogue Inputs

Calibrating Sensors

1 Which of the following components are analogue input devices? Tick the correct options.

A LDR ◯   **B** PTMS ◯   **C** Fixed resistor ◯

D PTBS ◯   **E** Thermistor ◯   **F** Tilt switch ◯

2 LDRs provide information on conditions that they're sensing. How is this expressed as a number?

....

3 Fill in the missing words to complete the following sentence.

An LDR has a .... reading when it's dark and a .... reading

when in bright light.

4 What can an analogue calibrator board allow you to do when using analogue sensors?

....

....

....

Compare Command

5 What do analogue sensors do in a PIC microcontroller system?

....

....

6 Draw a flowchart for a PIC programme that will switch lights on if the light level is less than or equal to 75.

Infra-red Remote Control

Infra-red and Types of Remote Control   AQA

1 Is the following statement **true** or **false**?

The most popular remote control used in the home is infra-red. ....

2 Name another type of remote control that can be used to open and close garage doors, or lock and unlock car doors.

....

Transmitting Signals   AQA

3 The basic concept with infra-red control is the use of invisible light. What does invisible light transmit?

....

Remote Controls   AQA

4 What does an infra-red remote control need in order to be able to bounce signals off walls and ceilings?

....

5 Fill in the missing words to complete the following sentence.

Infra-red remote controls have a working range of .... metres compared to

.... metres for radio frequency remote controls.

6 Which remote control system can transmit a signal through walls?

....

Infra-red Transmitter   AQA

7 Fill in the missing words to complete the following sentence.

A simple transmitter can be made by replacing the red LED with a .... power

infra-red ....

Remote Control Codes and Binary Code

1 The Sony S protocol system used in Sony remote controls uses seven-bit binary commands. Give an example of a seven-bit binary number.

....

2 a) How does the Sony S protocol system display the difference between a 1 and a 0 in a binary signal?

....

....

b) What is this method known as?

....

3 What two roles does the address code have in a remote control?

a) ....

....

b) ....

....

Binary Code   AQA

4 Fill in the missing words to complete the following sentence.

A .... is machine-readable information, usually of dark parallel vertical lines on a

white background, representing .... and ....

5 Give an everyday example of the use of binary code.

....

....

Microcontroller Infra-red Circuit

Infra-red Inputs and Outputs — AQA

1 Shown below is an infra-red receiver circuit.

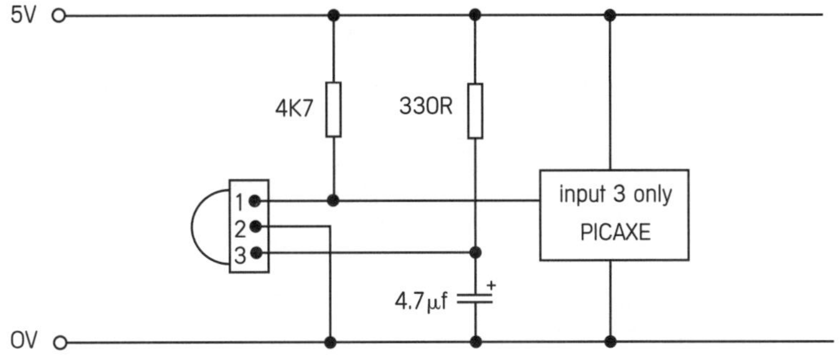

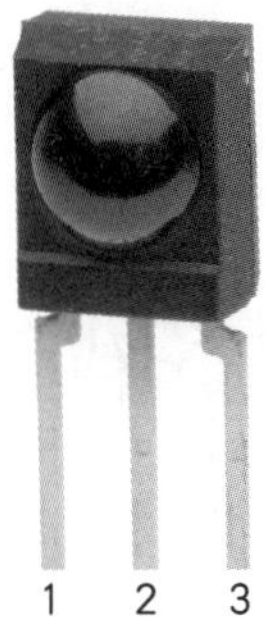

a) What is the purpose of the following components in the circuit above?

i) The 4K7 resistor. ....

ii) The 330R resistor. ....

iii) The 4.7μF capacitor. ....

b) Complete the sentences for the pin connections in the diagram above.

i) Pin 1 is connected to ....

ii) Pin 2 is connected to ....

iii) Pin 3 is connected to ....

Remote Controls — AQA

2 What are the two main components inside an infra-red remote control?

a) .... **b)** ....

3 Fill in the missing words to complete the following sentence.

When any button on an infra-red remote control is pressed, a ....

Is transmitted in the form of invisible .... light.

4 Is the following statement **true** or **false**?

Pressing any button on an infra-red remote control takes the PIC microcontroller input pin

connected to the infra-red receiver low. ....

PICAXE 08M Infra-red Receiver Circuit

1 Shown below is a PICAXE 08M infra-red receiver circuit.

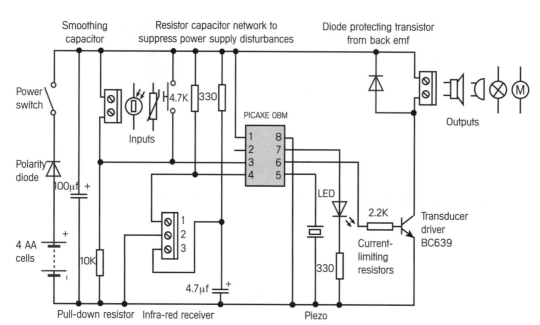

a) What type of PIC microcontroller is being used in the circuit above?

_____

b) Look at the PIC microcontroller and state what is connected to the 8 pins.

i) Pin 1 is connected to _____. **ii)** Pin 2 is connected to _____.

iii) Pin 3 is connected to _____. **iv)** Pin 4 is connected to _____.

v) Pin 5 is connected to _____. **vi)** Pin 6 is connected to _____.

vii) Pin 7 is connected to _____. **viii)** Pin 8 is connected to _____.

c) Name the two input devices shown in the circuit.

i) _____ **ii)** _____

d) Are the input devices digital or analogue devices? _____

e) Name the four output devices shown in the circuit:

i) _____ **ii)** _____

iii) _____ **iv)** _____

PICAXE 08M Infra-red Receiver Circuit

1 The diagram shows a PICAXE 08M infra-red receiver circuit.

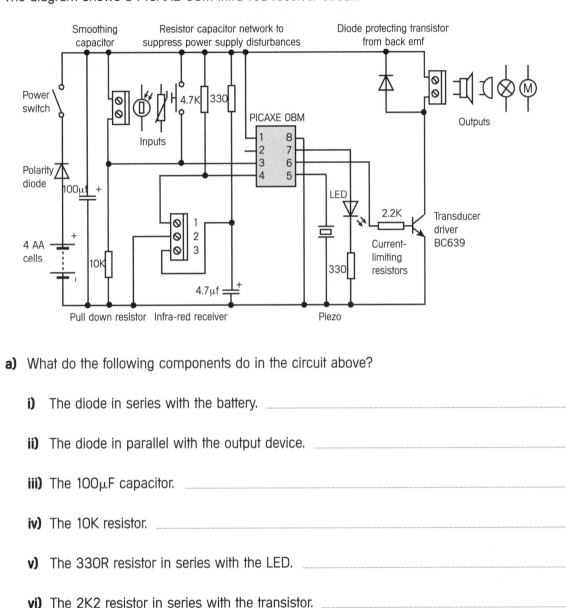

a) What do the following components do in the circuit above?

i) The diode in series with the battery. ....

ii) The diode in parallel with the output device. ....

iii) The 100μF capacitor. ....

iv) The 10K resistor. ....

v) The 330R resistor in series with the LED. ....

vi) The 2K2 resistor in series with the transistor. ....

b) What type of power switch is being used?

....

c) What is the voltage across the power rails?

....

d) The circuit is using three terminal blocks. What are the advantages of using terminal blocks?

....

Exam-style Questions

1. Complete the table below by giving the names and symbols of the components shown in the photographs. The first one has been done for you.

Component	Name	Symbol
	LED	
	Diode	
	Push to Make Switch	
	LDR	

2 Complete the following table. The first one has been done for you.

Name	Symbol	Input	Process	Output	Polar Component
Lamp				✔	No

Exam-style Questions

3 The following system diagram is for a road safety product.

LDR	→	Op-amp	→	Astable	→	Counter	→	LEDs

a) Which block represents an output stage?

....

b) Which block represents an input stage?

....

c) Which block could act as a comparator?

....

d) In which block would a 555 IC be used?

....

e) Which block changes an analogue signal into a digital signal?

....

f) Explain the difference between an analogue signal and a digital signal.

....

....

g) Draw the waveform of an analogue signal and a digital signal in the following boxes.

i) Analogue signal

ii) Digital signal

h) Explain why an analogue signal can confuse an electronic system that includes logic gates.

....

....

....

4 **a)** Label the leads of the LED shown below.

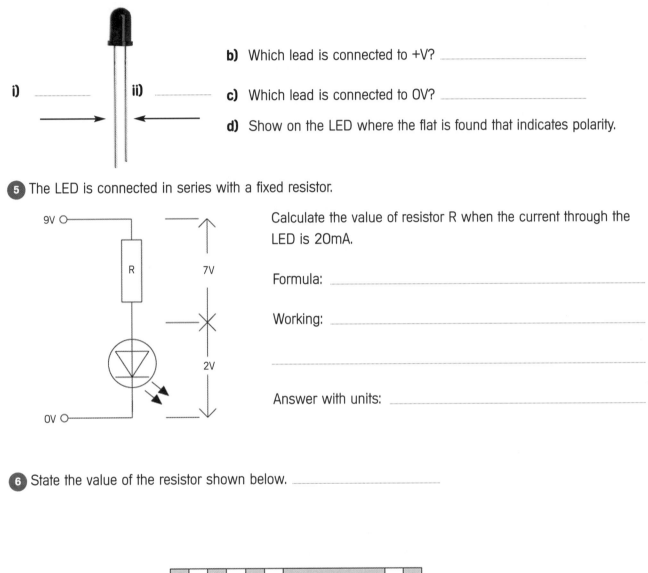

i) .... **ii)** ....

b) Which lead is connected to +V? ....

c) Which lead is connected to OV? ....

d) Show on the LED where the flat is found that indicates polarity.

5 The LED is connected in series with a fixed resistor.

Calculate the value of resistor R when the current through the LED is 20mA.

Formula: ....

Working: ....

....

Answer with units: ....

6 State the value of the resistor shown below. ....

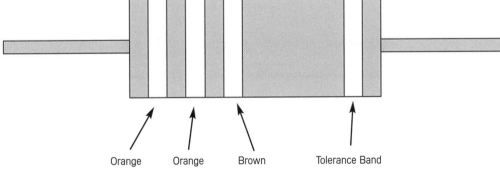

Orange   Orange   Brown   Tolerance Band

Exam-style Questions

7 A resistance of 600R is needed in a circuit but, as this value is not available, two resistors are to be used in series. Complete the diagram below by adding the values of two resistors from the E12 series to give the required 600R value.

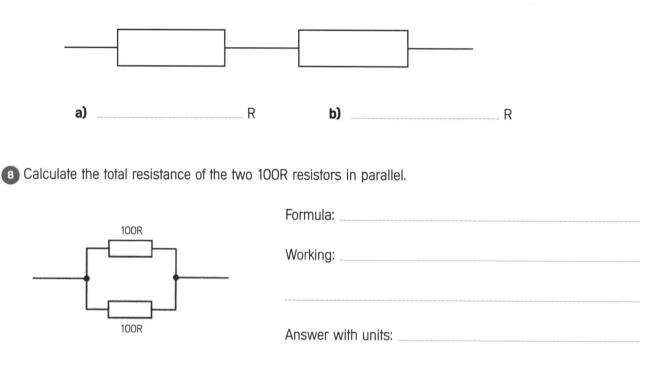

a) .... R   **b)** .... R

8 Calculate the total resistance of the two 100R resistors in parallel.

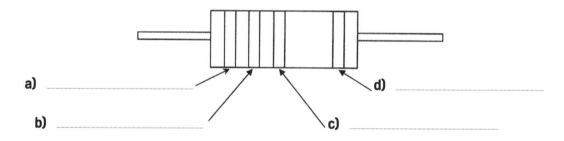

100R

100R

Formula: ....

Working: ....

....

Answer with units: ....

9 Complete the diagram below to show the colour code of a 680R resistor with a 5% tolerance.

a) ....

b) ....

c) ....

d) ....

10 Calculate the power rating of a resistor which has a voltage across it of 9V and a current of 20mA passing through it.

Formula: ....

Working: ....

....

Answer with units: ....

11 A circuit for a torch using a thyristor and an LED is shown.

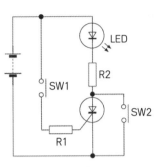

a) Circle the word that describes a thyristor circuit.

Astable   **Bistable**   **Monostable**

b) Explain what happens when the following actions are carried out in the order shown:

i) SW1 is pressed and released. ....

....

ii) SW2 is pressed and released. ....

....

c) The PCB layout of the circuit is shown opposite. When the circuit was built it did not work. Draw a circle around two mistakes that could be the cause of the problem.

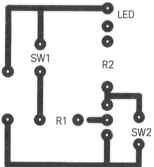

d) The PCB was produced using Computer Aided Design. List four advantages of using CAD for producing PCB layouts.

i) ....

ii) ....

iii) ....

iv) ....

Exam-style Questions

12 Complete the table below to describe what the labelled components do in the transistor circuit.

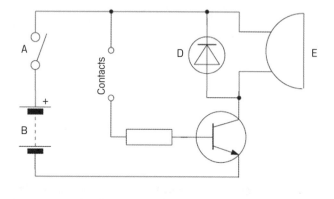

Component	What the Component Does in the Circuit
A	
B	
C	
D	
E	

13 Shown below is a modified transistor circuit with two changes.

Identify the changes made to the circuit and state what effect each one has on how the circuit works.

Change 1 ....

Effect ....

Change 2 ....

Effect ....

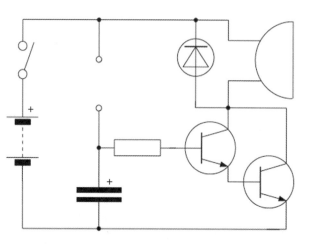

14 Shown below is an incomplete circuit diagram for a monostable using a 555 IC.

a) Complete the circuit diagram for the monostable by…

i) adding a 100K fixed resistor and a 22μF capacitor to pins 6 and 7.

ii) adding a fixed resistor and a suitable switch to pin 2 so as to trigger the 555 timer IC when the switch is pressed. Clearly label the resistor to show its value.

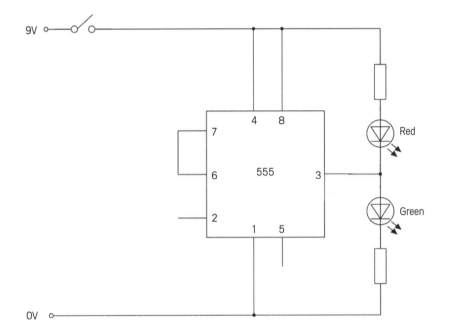

b) Describe what happens to the LEDs when the circuit is switched on and then triggered.

i) Circuit switched on ....

....

....

ii) Circuit triggered ....

....

....

15 Shown below is a circuit diagram for an astable using a 555 IC.

a) Add a buzzer connected to the output pin of the 555 IC, so that it will sound when the output goes high.

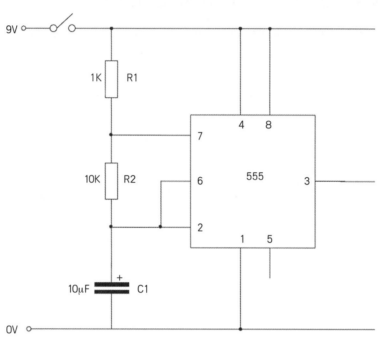

b) Calculate the frequency of the 555 IC astable.

Formula: ....

Working: ....

....

Answer with units: ....

c) Describe how the frequency of the circuit could be halved from its present value.

....

....

d) What component could be added to the circuit so that the frequency could be easily adjusted?

....

16 The circuit shows a 555 IC astable.

a) Circle the components that control the frequency of the pulses.

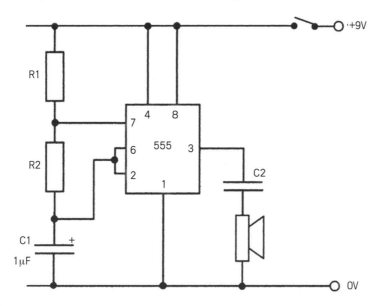

b) Shown below is the incomplete PCB design of the 555 IC astable circuit.

Complete the PCB by adding five tracks so that…

- Pin 8 is joined to the +V rail

- Pin 7 is joined between R1 and R2

- Pin 6 is joined to pin 2

- Pin 6 and 2 are joined between R2 and C1

- C2 is joined to the loudspeaker.

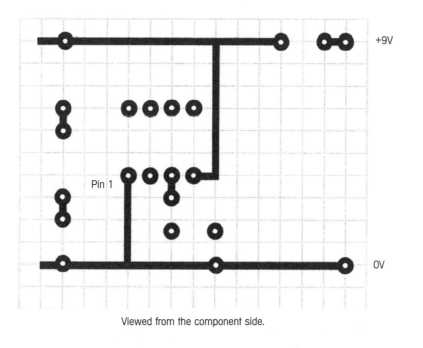

Viewed from the component side.

Exam-style Questions

17 Shown below is a light-sensing potential divider.

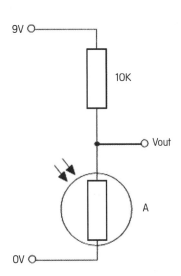

a) Name Component A ....

b) In bright light conditions, component A has a resistance of 5K. Calculate the value of Vout.

Formula: ....

Working: ....

....

Answer with units: ....

18 Shown below is an incomplete operational amplifier circuit. Complete the circuit diagram below by adding...

a) the light sensing potential divider shown above to the non-inverting input, to give a positive output from the amplifier when the sensor is in the dark.

b) a potential divider connected to the inverting input to give an adjustable reference voltage.

c) an LED with a resistor to indicate the output is high voltage.

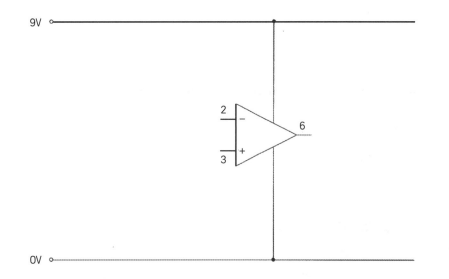

19 The diagram shows an incomplete circuit that is to switch on a 24V cooling fan.

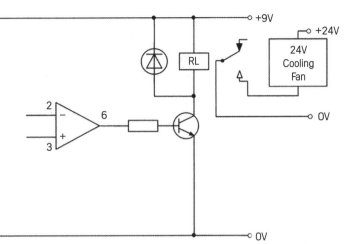

a) **i)** Give the name of the type of relay shown.

....

ii) Explain the reason for the need to include the relay in the circuit.

....

....

b) **i)** Complete the circuit above by adding:

- A method of producing a reference voltage of 4.5V at pin 2, including the value of any component used.

- A potential divider that includes a thermistor and a variable resistor on pin 3, that will cause pin 6 to go high when the temperature rises.

ii) Suggest a suitable voltage at pin 3 that will cause pin 6 to go high.

....

c) Calculate the voltage of pin 3 when the room temperature reaches 25°C and the variable resistor is set at 10K. The thermistor has a value of 8K at 25°C.

Formula: ....

Working: ....

....

Answer with units: ....

20 Complete the truth table for the OR gate shown below.

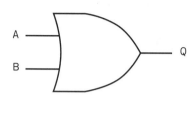

A	B	Q
0	0	
0	1	
1	0	
1	1	

21 The diagram below shows how an OR gate can be made from two NOR gates.

What is the logic state at Q when C is at logic 0? ....

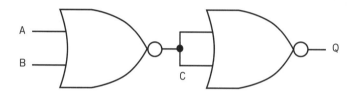

22 The circuit diagram below shows an IC containing four NOR gates. Complete the diagram so that…

a) two NOR gates are used to make an OR gate which is connected to the inputs A and B, and the output Q.

b) pin 14 is connected to +V and pin 7 is connected to 0V.

c) all unused inputs are connected to 0V.

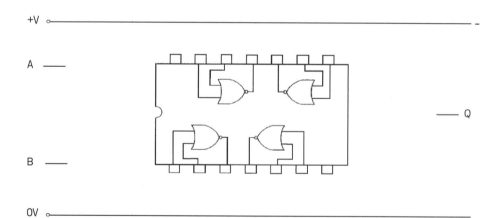

23 The lift in a department store is controlled using logic gates. The lift will only operate if…

- a person has requested the lift from another floor

- a floor has been chosen by a person in the lift

- the doorway is not obstructed.

The logic diagram for the system is shown below. Name the 3 logic gates.

a) A .... **b)** B .... **c)** C ....

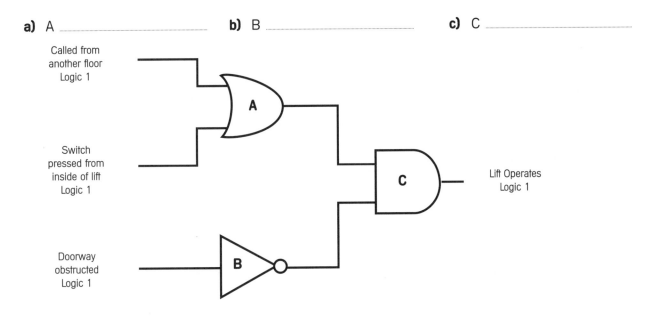

Called from another floor Logic 1

Switch pressed from inside of lift Logic 1

Lift Operates Logic 1

Doorway obstructed Logic 1

d) Complete the diagram below to show how the above system can be constructed using six NAND gates.

Called from another floor Logic 1

Switch pressed from inside of lift Logic 1

Lift Operates Logic 1

Doorway obstructed Logic 1

24 The owners of a dog kennel wish to install a heating system. It should come on automatically when it is dark or at any time when the temperature falls below a set level. They also require a manual override switch to allow them to switch the heating on at other times.

Note: When the conditions are met, the outputs from the sensors and the override switch will be high.

The block diagram below shows the heating system.

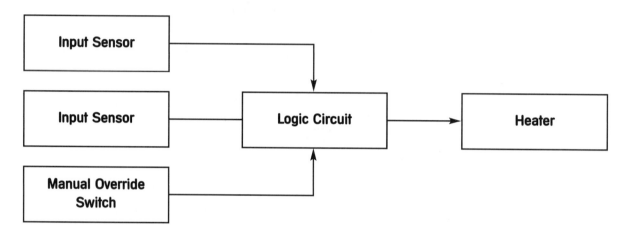

a) Complete the diagram below by filling in the empty boxes with the names of suitable input devices.

b) Using only 2 input NAND gates, complete the logic circuit to solve the problem.

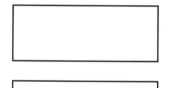

Heater

c) List four advantages of using only NAND gates to construct logic circuits.

i) ....

ii) ....

iii) ....

iv) ....

25 A PIC microcontroller is being used to count the lives for a steady hand game.

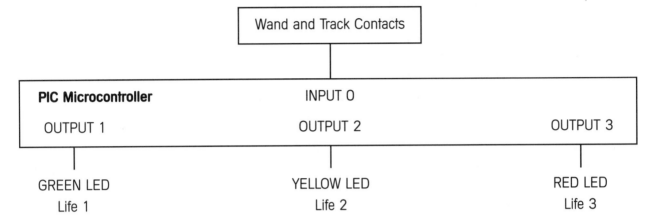

Using a programming method, design a PIC programme to satisfy the following conditions:

a) Each time the wand and track touch, the PIC switches on an LED in the sequence 1, 2 and 3. Once an LED is lit, it will stay on until reset.

b) Once the wand and track touch, the PIC will ignore any further contact for 2 seconds.

c) On the loss of the third life, all LEDs will switch off for 0.25 seconds and then switch on for 0.25 seconds. This is repeated three times.

d) The PIC programme will set back to no lives lost.

Exam-style Questions

26 A PIC microcontroller is being used to control the LEDs for a road safety product, which will be positioned on the ground to warn other motorists that a car has broken down.

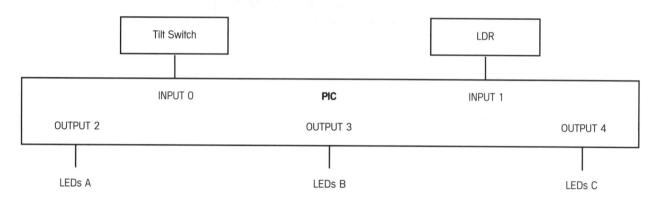

Using a programming method, design a PIC programme to satisfy the following conditions:

a) The circuit activates when the tilt switch is on and the light level around the LDR is 75 or less.

b) When activated, the LEDs flash in sequence A, B C and B (only one set of LEDs is on at a time). Each set of LEDs is to be on for 0.25 seconds. This repeats 10 times.

c) All the LEDs then come on together for 0.5 seconds and go off for 0.5 seconds. This sequence is repeated 5 times.

d) The programme repeats until deactivated.

27 Electronic games have changed the way we spend our leisure time.

a) Describe how electronic games have changed in recent years.

....

....

....

b) Explain the impact electronic games are said to have had on personal health and on social and family life.

i) Personal Health

....

....

....

ii) Social and Family Life

....

....

....

c) The rapid rate of change of electronic products means that some products soon become obsolete. What advantages does this have for the manufacturer?

....

....

....

d) Many electronic products use batteries. Why is it important to dispose of batteries correctly and safely?

....

....

....

Exam-style Questions

28 Health and safety is very important when making a PCB due to the many hazards. Identify the precautions to be taken when carrying out the following tasks:

a) Using an ultraviolet light box.

Precaution: ....

....

b) Developing the PCB.

Precaution: ....

....

c) Etching the PCB in ferric chloride.

Precaution: ....

....

d) Drilling the holes on the PCB.

Precaution: ....

....

e) Using a disc sanding machine to clean up the edges of the PCB.

Precaution: ....

....

f) Soldering the components to the PCB.

Precaution: ....

....

29 Give two reasons why mains electricity should be avoided when choosing a power supply for your project.

a) ....

b) ....